The Bible Pageant Series

—»»-»»-»»-«-«-«-«—

BRAVE PIONEERS

CONQUERING HEROES

KINGS AND QUEENS

THE MIGHTY PRINCE

WARRIORS OF THE CROSS

THE BIBLE PAGEANT

Volume Three

KINGS AND QUEENS

The Bible Pageant

by MERLIN L. NEFF, Ph. D.

VOLUME THREE

KINGS AND QUEENS

Scripture in the Stories from J. M. Powis Smith and
Edgar J. Goodspeed, The Bible, an American Translation

PACIFIC PRESS PUBLISHING ASSN., Mountain View, California
Brookfield, Illinois   Cristobal, Canal Zone   Omaha, Nebraska
Portland, Oregon

EXPLANATION

Wherever conversation is employed in the Bible stories, the words of the characters are taken directly from the Scriptures. However, the language of *The Bible, an American Translation,* by J. M. Powis Smith and Edgar J. Goodspeed, is the translation used, with the kind permission of the University of Chicago Press. This translation offers the young readers modern language that is easily understood without in any way marring the beauty or inspiration of the word.

Library of Congress
Catalog Card Number 47-20254

Eighth Printing

81,000 previously printed

1954

PACIFIC
PRESS
PUB.
ASSN.

PRINTED
IN U·S·A·

CONTENTS

PREFACE

The pageant of Old Testament heroes is completed with this volume, featuring the adventures of Israel's and Judah's kings and queens. We meet Saul, the first monarch of the kingdom, a tall and handsome warrior, who failed in the task he was dedicated to accomplish. We watch David from the youthful days of sheepherding to the time when he makes his son, Solomon, king in his stead.

Elijah, the fighter for God's truth, and Elisha, the prophet of wonders, move through the pages of the Bible story. They are courageous men, who defy wicked kings and heathen enemies.

When the nation disobeys the commandments of God and falls before the armies from the north and the east, we find young men who meet the test of allegiance to their religion. Daniel and his three companions, Hezekiah, Queen Esther, and thousands of unnamed Jews, refuse to worship idols and compromise their faith. There is glory even in the hour of defeat and exile.

The seven story chapters, centering in the experiences of the Barrett children and their friend, Captain Timothy Lane, continue to enlarge the panorama of the Old Testament with facts about shepherd life, customs and festivals of Bible times, and the glories of the king's treasures. How the divine prophecies were fulfilled in the annals of history is another feature of the narrative.

As youth behold true character and see the adventurous men and women who served their God in days of old, may they likewise dedicate themselves today to the service of the King of kings.   THE AUTHOR.

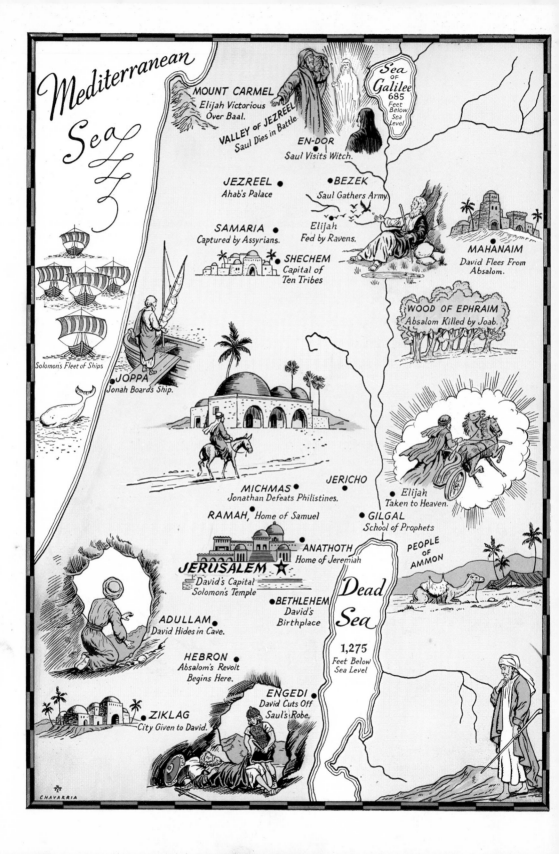

Mediterranean Sea

MOUNT CARMEL
Elijah Victorious
Over Baal.

VALLEY of JEZREEL
Saul Dies in Battle

EN-DOR
Saul Visits Witch.

Sea
OF
Galilee
685
Feet
Below
Sea
Level

JEZREEL
Ahab's Palace

BEZEK
Saul Gathers Army.

SAMARIA
Captured by Assyrians.

Elijah
Fed by Ravens.

SHECHEM
Capital of
Ten Tribes

MAHANAIM
David Flees From
Absalom.

WOOD OF EPHRAIM
Absalom Killed by Joab.

Solomon's Fleet of Ships

JOPPA
Jonah Boards Ship.

JERICHO

MICHMAS
Jonathan Defeats Philistines.

Elijah
Taken to Heaven.

RAMAH, Home of Samuel

GILGAL
School of Prophets

PEOPLE
OF
AMMON

ANATHOTH
Home of Jeremiah

JERUSALEM ☆
David's Capital
Solomon's Temple

Dead
Sea

BETHLEHEM
David's
Birthplace

ADULLAM
David Hides in Cave.

1,275
Feet Below
Sea Level

HEBRON
Absalom's Revolt
Begins Here.

ENGEDI
David Cuts Off
Saul's Robe.

ZIKLAG
City Given to David.

CHAVARRIA

Black Sea

Caspian Sea

ARARAT

Mediterranean Sea

Solomon's Navy   Cedars of Lebanon

PALESTINE   {This Area Shown on Preceding Page.

•DAMASCUS
Home of Naaman the Leper.

NINEVEH
Jonah Preached.

SHUSHAN
•Queen Esther

BABYLON
Daniel and
Three Companions

EGYPT

Solomon's Copper Mines

Solomon's Navy

Red Sea

Persian Gulf

N
W   E
S

Queen of Sheba
Came From Ethiopia.

© P. P. P. A.

The Barrett twins, **Bette** and **Roy**, read the Bible stories of Old Testament heroes such as David, Daniel, Ruth, Esther, and Joseph, and relived their thrilling adventures.

PROVERBS, WARRIORS,
and THANKSGIVING BASKETS

E VERYTHING was topsy-turvy in the Lane kitchen. Bette Barrett was dancing about excitedly as she helped Mrs. Lane pack fruit in gift baskets. Roy, Bette's eleven-year-old twin, was polishing big red apples with a cloth while Captain Lane wrapped fruit and nuts in bright-colored cellophane. The door swung open suddenly, letting in a blast of frosty November air, and with it came Dick Barrett loaded with boxes. "Look out," the youth warned. "There are five fresh pumpkin pies in these boxes. Handle with care!"

"Go ahead and drop one," called Roy, teasing his brother. "I'll salvage it. Um-m! When I think what I could do with one of mother's fresh pumpkin pies right now, you're hardly safe with that stack of boxes."

"Well, avoid temptation, Roy," said the elder Barrett. "Help me unload these pies on the table. Oh, yes, Mrs. Lane, mother says if you want any more canned fruit or walnuts for the baskets to send for them. She has plenty."

"Thank you, Dick," replied the lady, as she peeked at one of the golden brown pies. "It looks as if we'll have plenty of every-

(11)

The Pilgrims, braving cold and danger, went to church on the first Thanksgiving Day, thus remembering God as the Giver of their blessings and thanking Him for His protection.

thing for the holiday baskets. Don't you think so, Timothy?"

"Yes, my dear," returned the man. "From the amount of good food you have around this kitchen I'd say we could feed a small city." The captain broke a cooky in two and gave a piece to Chips, his brown cocker spaniel, who was begging piteously for a share of the goodies that tantalized his nose.

It had become a tradition in the Lane home for the captain and his wife to prepare Thanksgiving baskets for a dozen needy families in the community, and they had shared the joy of giving with the three young Barretts. The Barrett home was on the other side of Maple Street, a half block away. Bette and her mother supplied the cakes, cookies, and canned fruit, while Roy and Dick worked with the captain making attractive gift baskets.

"Only two days until Thanksgiving," announced Bette. "That means the school pageant is tomorrow night."

"You should remember, Bette, since you're Priscilla," teased Roy.

" 'Why don't you speak for yourself, John?' " returned Bette, quoting the famous line from Longfellow's poem.

"What program are you giving this year?" asked Mrs. Lane.

"It's the story of the Pilgrim Fathers' first Thanksgiving," explained the girl. "Dick is an Indian who comes to the feast."

"Don't forget I'm Captain Miles Standish," added Roy.

"The old soldier who fights Indians," teased Dick.

"When we think of the hardships that the Pilgrims endured, I wonder if we are as thankful as we should be for all our blessings," mused the captain, after listening to the chatter of conversation.

"Our thanks is like a drop in the bucket compared with the good things we receive," agreed Dick. "And a pretty small drop at that."

"If one begins counting, I'd say I'm thankful first of all for a wonderful mother, a real dad, and a happy home." The words tumbled out as Bette counted her blessings on three fingers.

"While you're mentioning it, I'm thankful to live in a free country," Roy declared. "We should be particularly grateful for the fathers of our country who helped to give us liberty."

"How right you are, Roy," agreed the captain. "Liberty is a scarce article in the world today."

"I'll add a few more 'thank you's' to the list," Dick put in quickly. "A good education, fine libraries, clean recreation and good times, the church, and the Bible—those are a few of the

things I'm grateful to have. Perhaps our thanks isn't 'a drop in the bucket,' after all."

"Where do you suppose we get the saying, 'A drop in the bucket'?" asked Bette, as she set a finished basket on the floor.

"Don't you know, Bette?" asked Captain Lane. "That's in the Bible."

The man knew his Bible better than any other person the Barretts had ever met. He had made the Old Testament adventures so interesting the three Barretts were reading it through. He was helping them by explaining the history, geography, and customs of the people of long ago.

"We get many expressions in our language from the Bible, don't we, captain?"

"Indeed we do, Roy. There are scores of common phrases such as 'the widow's mite,' 'the fat of the land,' 'the little foxes that spoil the vines,' and 'a still small voice.' In fact," the man continued, "no other book has influenced our language as much as the Bible."

"Isn't 'the apple of his eye,' from the Bible?" queried Mrs. Lane, placing two red apples in a basket as she spoke.

"Of course it is, my dear," replied the man, "and also 'a thorn in the flesh,' 'stolen waters are sweet,' and 'the eye of a needle.' Once when I was in college, my English teacher assigned us the task of finding ten sayings from the Bible in current magazines and newspapers. I remember the class had more than one hundred fifty different ones when they were finally checked by the professor."

"Who said: 'Is there any taste in the white of an egg?'" asked Roy.

Everything was topsy-turvy in the Lane kitchen. Everyone was busy preparing Thanksgiving baskets.

W. WILKE, ARTIST

"That's not in the Bible," said Bette. "It sounds too modern."

"Didn't they have eggs in those days?" chided Roy, as he tossed an apple toward Bette, who had to catch it in self-defense.

"Don't say it isn't in the Bible, Bette," cautioned Captain Lane gently. "Remember, that book is never out of date." Then turning to Roy, the man continued: "You'll find that question in the Book of books, all right. When Job's three friends came to visit him in time of suffering, he asked them about the taste of an egg white."

"Speaking of three friends," Roy spoke up quickly, "I've been reading about David's three brave warriors or knights. Boy, did they have some exciting adventures!"

"What did they do?" asked Dick. "I haven't gotten that far in the story of David."

"I'm not too sure of their names," said Roy; "but the leader was so strong that he cornered eight hundred enemy soldiers and killed them singlehanded."

"That was the chief of David's captains," Captain Lane asserted. "I believe his name was Adino."

"Another was Eleazar, son of Dodo," Roy continued. "That was a strange name I couldn't forget. He fought the Philistines all one day, and in the evening he did not lay down his sword because he had held it so long his hand was cramped and he couldn't release it."

"One time David longed for a drink of water from the old well in his home town of Bethlehem. His three mighty men heard him say he wished for a drink, and they risked their lives to go through the Philistine lines to get a jug of water. When they brought it to David, he realized the danger they had faced and he would not drink it; it seemed as precious as their lives."

"That sounds interesting," declared Bette. "I can hardly wait to get the stories and read every word of them for myself."

"One other brave fellow always interested me, Roy," continued the captain. "He was Benaiah, one of thirty warriors whom David honored. One day this young man killed a lion and her two cubs in a pit. What makes the adventure more daring is that it had been snowing. I can imagine him sliding down the side of the pit, which was slick and icy. The snarling lion must have been ready to jump on him, but he was able to attack first."

"Speaking of lions, Captain Tim, isn't there a Bible proverb about a dead lion?" asked Dick.

"You're probably thinking of the one written by Solomon: 'A living dog is better than a dead lion.'"

"Meaning that you're better alive as a common person than famous, but dead," suggested practical-minded Mrs. Lane. "And speaking of proverbs, there's one prescription by King Solomon I always like when I am blue. He said: 'A merry heart doeth good like a medicine.'"

"That's how your smiles affect me," said the man gallantly. "But seriously, the Bible has become a part of our everyday life. It even enters into national celebrations. When I was reading the story of the prophet Samuel the other evening, I found that the children of Israel shouted the same words the people of England chant today when a king is crowned. Do you remember what the people said when Samuel introduced Saul, the first king of Israel, to the nation?"

"It was, 'God save the king,'" answered Bette Barrett.

Soon the decorated Thanksgiving baskets were loaded into Captain Lane's car, and he and the two Barrett boys were off to spread holiday happiness to several homes.

"That shout has come down through the centuries and is heard at the coronation ceremonies of kings in modern times."

"It looks as if we are all ready to send the Thanksgiving baskets on their way," broke in Mrs. Lane, who was putting the finishing touches on the last basket. "Are the three 'basketeers' ready to take them?"

"That's our principal reason for staying in the kitchen, my dear," the man replied. "Usually I avoid this spot, especially if there are any dishes to wash."

"You should see Roy and Dick scamper out of the house if they think they may be drafted for kitchen duty," said Bette, pointing an accusing finger at her brothers.

"Let's take the baskets and leave," urged Roy playfully. And soon the gaily decorated baskets were loaded into Captain Lane's car, and he and the two Barrett boys were off to spread happiness in homes that might have otherwise had a bleak Thanksgiving Day.

"On Thanksgiving morning Roy and I are hiking out to Bear Lake to see the speedboat races." Dick was speaking as the car rolled along the avenue.

"I'm taking my new motion-picture camera," added Roy.

"You'll have a good time, I'm sure," returned the man, who knew a great deal about taking pictures. "Be sure to check your light meter, and don't shift your camera or take sweeping shots."

"Roy's learning after his first mistake," Dick confided. "He had the whole family dizzy trying to look at his pictures of horseback riding at Hillcrest Farm."

"Don't criticize," warned the younger brother. "Look how you cut off mother's and dad's heads when you tried to take a picture of us in the park."

"We're almost at Widow Beasley's house. It's time to check those baskets and see that we have the right one ready." The captain's words turned the boys to the task of passing out good will to a dozen homes in the city, a happy time for everyone who took part.

"LONG LIVE the KING!"

1 SAMUEL 9:1 to 11:15

"GIVE us a king to judge us. Give us a king to judge us." The words of the leaders of the twelve tribes of Israel continued to ring in the ears of Samuel, the prophet, long after the throng had left his house at Ramah. The prophet had been a faithful judge over the people for many years, and now he was growing old. He had appointed his two sons to rule, but they disobeyed God and robbed the people.

Samuel did not hurry to settle the issue, for he wanted the Lord to direct in the choice of a king. One day the prophet received a message from God saying: "About this time to-morrow I will send you a man out of the land of Benjamin and you shall anoint him to be a leader of My people Israel. He shall deliver My people from the power of the Philistines; for I have seen the affliction of My people and their cry has come to Me."

Of course, Samuel was anxious to know whom the Lord had chosen to be king. The next morning the prophet arose early and went to the gate of the city to watch for the man who would be ruler of Israel.

Now Saul, the son of a powerful and wealthy chief named Kish, had been searching for some animals that had strayed

(21)

In the streets of the cities of Israel, such as this modern setting, people were talking of the new king that would rule Israel.

from his father's farm. For three days the young man and his servant had been hiking through the hill country, but they had not found the lost asses. The servant suggested that they stop at the town of Ramah to seek the advice of the prophet.

As the two men approached the city, they met some girls carrying empty pitchers who were on their way to get water from the town well. When Saul asked them where he might find the man of God, the girls replied that the prophet was in the city and that he was going to a religious service that would be followed by a feast. As Saul and his servant hurried into the city, Samuel saw them. When he beheld the tall, handsome youth, the Lord said to the prophet: "Behold the man of whom I spoke to you! He it is who shall bear rule over My people." Saul approached Samuel, the prophet or seer of Israel, and asked: "Pray tell me, where is the house of the seer?"

"I am the seer," replied Samuel; "go up before me to the high place, for you shall eat with me today; and in the morning I will gladly further your journey, and tell you all that is on your mind."

The bashful young man could scarcely believe the words of Samuel. The youth who started from home to look for lost animals never dreamed of going to a feast as the guest of the prophet. "Am I not a Benjaminite, from the smallest of the tribes of Israel," said Saul humbly, "and is not my family the least of all the families of the tribe of Benjamin? Why then have you spoken to me after this manner?"

Samuel did not wait to explain, for if he did they would be late at the assembly. Therefore, he hurried the son of Kish to the hall where there were about thirty guests, and he placed

The leaders of the people assembled before Samuel at Ramah and requested that they be ruled by a king like other nations. They shouted: "Give us a king to judge us!"

the young man at the head of the table. After the feast Saul went to the house of Samuel and spent the night.

At daybreak the next morning, Samuel called Saul and helped him prepare for the homeward journey. The prophet accompanied the young man beyond the city wall, and after the servant had been sent on ahead, Samuel took a flask of oil and poured it upon Saul's head and kissed him. Then Samuel explained to Saul that the Lord had appointed him to rule over Israel. The prophet also told him that the lost animals had been found and returned to the farm.

Saul went on his way with a strange thrill in his heart. He could scarcely believe that he had been anointed king over Israel. As he walked toward his home he decided that he would keep the matter a close secret until the proper time arrived.

Soon the day came when Samuel, the judge, called all the leaders of the nation together to tell them of their new king. The prophet asked the tribes of Israel to pass before him one by one, and under the Lord's direction the tribe of Benjamin was chosen. Then the families of the tribe of Benjamin passed in review, and Saul's family was picked. Finally, a man of the family of Kish was selected, and, behold, it was Saul. When the young man was brought before the people, they saw that he was tall and strong. In fact, he was so tall that most of the men came only to his shoulders. Samuel spoke to the people, saying: "Do you see him whom the Lord has chosen? for there is not his peer among all the people."

"Long live the king!" shouted all the people.

After the servant had been sent on ahead, Samuel took a flask of oil and poured it upon Saul's head. Then Samuel explained to Saul that the Lord had appointed him king.

W. WILKE, ARTIST

Samuel brought Saul to the people, saying: "Do you see him whom the Lord has cho-sen? for there is not his peer among all the people." "Long live the king!" they shouted.

Samuel described the kind of kingdom the people would have. He recorded the business of choosing a king in a book and laid it with the other books in the house of God. Then the prophet dismissed the crowd, and the people went home. The Lord touched the hearts of some of the brave men, and they immediately followed Saul. Others, however, were jealous and despised the new king. They whispered among themselves: "How shall this man save us?"

About a month after the coronation of Saul the savage people of Ammon threatened the children of Israel who lived at Jabesh on the east side of the Jordan River. Nahash, the savage king of the Ammonites, declared he would make peace, but only on one condition. To the men of Israel he said: "On this condition will I make terms with you: that I gouge out the right eye of every one of you, thereby making it a reproach against all Israel."

"Give us seven days respite," said Israel's leaders. Then they sent messengers through the land, calling for help. When Saul heard the terrible news, he killed a yoke of oxen and cut their bodies into pieces and sent the pieces to all the tribes of Israel by messengers who said: "Whoever does not come forth after Saul and after Samuel, so shall it be done to his oxen."

The people rallied quickly, and 330,000 men met King Saul at Bezek. After dividing his warriors into three companies, Saul marched them eastward until they crossed the Jordan River and faced the enemy. From morning until midday the armies fought, and the Ammonites were defeated and scattered.

Israel was proud of their brave king. As the warriors celebrated the victory, some of them remembered the words of those who had despised Saul. They hurried to Samuel, saying: "Who is he that says, 'Saul shall not reign over us?' Bring the men that we may put them to death."

But King Saul said: "There shall not a man be put to death today, for today the Lord has brought about deliverance in Israel." Instead of taking the glory to himself, Saul gave thanks to God for victory over the enemy.

Samuel, who had witnessed the battle, called the people together at Gilgal, the historic town where the children of Israel made their first camp after entering the land of Canaan. Samuel stood before the people and said:

"See, I have yielded to your plea in all that you have said to me and have appointed a king over you. Behold now the king

Samuel described the kind of kingdom the people would have. He recorded the business of choosing a king in a book and laid it with the other books in God's house.

who is to go out and in before you; but as for me, I am old and gray, and my sons are here with you; and I have conducted myself before you from my youth unto this day."

The people held a grand celebration and offered thanks to the Lord for His blessings.

The DISOBEDIENT KING

1 SAMUEL 13:1 to 15:35

IN the hour of victory King Saul should have led his army against the other enemies that threatened Israel, for by this move he might have given freedom to all his people. However, the king disbanded the main body of his army, keeping only two thousand soldiers with him at Michmas. He placed another thousand warriors under the command of his son, Jonathan, who faced the warlike Philistines at Gibeah.

The Israelites had been cruelly oppressed by the Philistines during the days of the judges. The enemy had taken all the swords and spears from the men of Israel and had left no metal workers in the country to make more weapons. The farmers were forced to go to the land of the Philistines to sharpen their plows and hoes. Therefore the soldiers of King Saul were at a great disadvantage in battle. But, in spite of this sad plight, the king made no effort to arm his men with swords and spears; so they were forced to go on fighting with bows and slings, with axes and hoes.

In the second year of Saul's reign Jonathan grew impatient because his father would not attack the enemy. The bold Philistines came with thousands of chariots, horsemen, and soldiers,

(29)

Jonathan and his armor-bearer moved out of sight of the Philistines and made their way forward stealthily along a difficult path.

W. WILKE, ARTIST

challenging the men of Israel to fight. Saul's army acted cowardly; the warriors slipped away from the camp and hid in caves and among the rocks of the hills.

When Jonathan saw the Philistines encamped at Michmas, a rocky hill across the valley from the crags where the Israelites were hiding, he went into action. Trusting in the power of God to help him deliver the nation, he said to the faithful youth who carried his armor: "Come, let us go over to the post of the Philistines, that is on the other side yonder."

Without telling anyone else of his plan, Jonathan took his armor-bearer and made his way down the mountainside, across the valley, and up the steep cliffs to where the Philistine fortress stood. When the enemy guards saw the two soldiers from Israel climbing up the rocks, they said: "Look! Hebrews are coming out of the holes where they have hidden themselves." The guards then challenged Jonathan and his armor-bearer, saying: "Come up to us, we have something to tell you."

Jonathan accepted the challenge as a sign that God was with him. He and his armor-bearer moved out of sight of the Philistines and made their way forward stealthily along a steep and difficult path. Suddenly they reached the summit, overpowered the guards, and killed about twenty Philistines.

Terror took hold of the enemy forces, and, to make matters worse for them, an earthquake shook the mountain. The Philistines were in panic and began a hasty retreat. When King Saul heard the noise and saw the enemy in tumult, he commanded his men to attack. Many of the soldiers who had deserted came out of hiding and joined in the battle. Soon the Philistines were routed and driven back to their own country.

"The Lord anointed you king over Israel, and the Lord sent you on a mission," said Samuel to King Saul after the battle. "Why then did you not obey the voice of the Lord?"

After this, Saul chose the bravest men he could find for his army, and he appointed his cousin, Abner, to be his general. In successful battle he defeated the armies of Moab, Ammon, and Edom; but there was another enemy that had long troubled Israel, the Amalekites. When Samuel saw how successful the king was in battle, he sent Saul a message commanding him to make war against this wicked nation. The aged prophet reminded the king of the cruel attack the tribe of Amalek had made on the children of Israel when Moses led the people through the desert. God had promised that this nation would someday be destroyed for its terrible deeds. Samuel believed that the time had arrived for the enemy to be exterminated. Therefore the prophet said to Saul: "The Lord sent me to anoint you to be king over His people Israel. Now then listen to the words of the Lord. Thus says the Lord of hosts: 'I will punish Amalek for what he did to Israel, in that he opposed him on the way, when he came up out of Egypt. Now go and attack Amalek and utterly destroy him and all that he has, and spare him not, but slaughter both man and woman, child and infant, ox and sheep, camel and ass.'"

With an army of 210,000 men Saul marched against the Amalekites. In a brilliant victory he destroyed most of the tribe; but he spared Agag, the king, and the soldiers of Israel were allowed to keep the best of the sheep, lambs, oxen, and calves. Selfish King Saul was determined to keep this booty in spite of God's command to destroy everything.

Early in the morning Samuel met Saul and his army at Carmel. The king said proudly to the prophet: "Blessed be you of the Lord! I have fulfilled the command of the Lord."

"What then is this bleating of sheep in my ears and the lowing of cattle which I hear?" said Samuel.

"They have brought them from the Amalekites," said Saul, "for the people spared the best of the sheep and the oxen to sacrifice to the Lord your God; and the rest we have completely destroyed." Poor, weak Saul! He tried to blame his soldiers for his own disobedience.

"Desist! and let me tell you what the Lord spoke to me last night," said Samuel to Saul. "The Lord anointed you king over Israel, and the Lord sent you on a mission and said, 'Go and completely wipe out the sinners, the Amalekites, and fight against them until you have consumed them.' Why then did you not obey the voice of the Lord and why did you fling yourselves upon the spoil and do that which was evil in the sight of the Lord?"

Saul attempted to excuse himself by saying that he had kept the best of the sheep and cattle to make a sacrifice to the Lord. But Samuel answered:

"Does the Lord delight in burnt offerings and sacrifices
As much as in obedience to the voice of the Lord?
Behold, to obey is better than sacrifice,
And to hearken, than the fat of rams."

Then Saul said to Samuel: "I have sinned; for I have transgressed the command of the Lord and your words, because I feared the people and listened to their voice. Now therefore pardon my sin and turn back with me, that I may worship the Lord."

But Samuel said to Saul: "I will not turn back with you; for you have rejected the word of the Lord and the Lord has rejected you from being king over Israel."

Then the valiant old prophet sent for Agag, the cruel king of the Amalekites, whom Saul had spared. Samuel took the sword and destroyed this wicked enemy with his own hands. Saul was rejected as king of Israel because he had disobeyed. The young man thought that his own way was better than God's plan. He failed because he did not believe that "to obey is better than sacrifice." Samuel left Saul and only once did the prophet and the dishonored king ever meet again.

3

DAVID, GIANT KILLER and KING

1 SAMUEL 16:1 to 17:58

WHEN Samuel returned to his house at Ramah, he grieved because Saul had failed to obey God. The aged prophet loved the young king, and he had dreamed that this youth would lead Israel on to victory; but now there was no hope for his success. Soon the Lord spoke to Samuel: "How long will you grieve over Saul, since I have rejected him from being king over Israel? Fill your horn with oil and go. I will send you to Jesse the Bethlehemite; for I have discovered for Myself a king among his sons."

The prophet was afraid and said: "How can I go, since Saul will hear of it and kill me?"

Then the Lord told Samuel to journey to Bethlehem with an offering. When he arrived in the town he was to make a sacrifice at a special ceremony and invite Jesse to attend.

The prophet came to Bethlehem, and the chief men of the village saw him. Trembling with fear, they said to Samuel: "Is your coming peaceable?"

"Yes, I have come to sacrifice to the Lord," said Samuel. So the men of the town gathered at the altar to worship God, and Jesse and his sons were present.

Now, Jesse was the son of Obed. We remember that Obed

(35)

David took five smooth stones from the brook and, with his sling ready, advanced toward Giant Goliath.

was the son of Ruth, the gleaner who married Boaz. Jesse was a sheep rancher, and he had eight sons who helped him tend the flocks.

After the sacrifice had been offered, the prophet desired to see the sons of Jesse. Beginning with Eliab, the eldest, Samuel studied the young men carefully. He was pleased with the appearance of Eliab, for he was strong and handsome. The prophet would have anointed him king of Israel at once, but the Lord said: "Do not look at his appearance or the height of his stature, since I have rejected him; for the Lord does not see as man sees, for man looks on the outward appearance, but the Lord looks at the heart."

Two, three, four! The sons came before Samuel one by one, but none of these was selected as king. Five, six, seven! They, too, passed by and were not accepted. Now the prophet was troubled, and he said to Jesse: "Are these all the young men?"

"There is still the youngest," he said, "but just now he is shepherding the flock."

"Send and bring him," said Samuel, "for we will not sit down until he arrives."

David, the ruddy shepherd boy, was brought in from the field and presented to Samuel. When the prophet saw the keen eyes and beautiful countenance of the youth, he heard God say: "Arise, anoint him, for this is he." Then Samuel took the horn of oil and anointed the shepherd boy to be king while his brothers and his father stood and watched the strange ceremony.

In the meantime, Saul became sad and despondent. In fact, he showed so many signs of madness that his servants proposed that a skillful harp player be found whose soft music might

David, the ruddy shepherd boy, was brought in from the field and presented to Samuel.
When the prophet saw the youth, he heard God say: "Arise, anoint him, for this is he."

soothe the king's troubled mind. Saul liked the suggestion and said, "Provide me now with a man who plays well, and bring him to me."

Thereupon one of the young men answered and said: "Behold, I have seen a son of Jesse the Bethlehemite who is skillful in playing and a man of unusual power, a warrior, judicious in speech, a distinguished-looking man, and the Lord is with him."

Saul sent messengers to Jesse requesting that David be allowed to come and play before him. So the father sent the shepherd boy to Saul's court bearing presents to the ruler. David played beautiful melodies on his harp, many of which he had composed while he herded sheep in the hills. Perhaps he sang the poem that later became the Shepherd Psalm.

"The Lord is my shepherd; I shall not want;
In green pastures He makes me lie down;
Beside refreshing waters He leads me.
He gives me new life;
He guides me in paths of righteousness for
    His name's sake.
Even though I walk in the darkest valley,
I fear no harm; for Thou are with me;
Thy rod and Thy staff—they comfort me.
Thou layest a table before me in the presence
    of my enemies;
Thou anointest my head with oil; my cup overflows.
Surely goodness and kindness shall follow
    me all the days of my life;
And I shall dwell in the house of the Lord to an old age."

Saul was refreshed by the music, and his heart was happy once more. He liked David and made him his armor-bearer, a high honor for a servant of the monarch.

Now, the Philistines continued to make attacks on the men of Israel. The enemy camped on one mountain, while Israel's army was stationed on another across the valley from the enemy. Every day a mighty champion from the camp of the Philistines marched down into the Valley of Elah and made fun of the Israelites. His name was Goliath, and he was a giant about ten feet tall. He wore a helmet and a coat of mail made of bronze, and his spear and sword were of great weight. Every morning and evening for forty days he stood before the soldiers of Israel ridiculing them and saying, "I challenge the ranks of Israel this day, give me a man that we may fight together."

When Saul and all Israel heard the words of the Philistine, they were terrified and their hearts failed within them.

One day while David was playing, Saul seized
his spear and hurled it at the youthful harp
player, saying: "I will pin David to the wall."

W. WILKE, ARTIST

In the meantime David had returned home to help his father care for the sheep so that his older brothers could join the army of Saul. One day Jesse said to David: "Take now for your brothers an ephah of this parched grain and these ten loaves and take them quickly to the camp to your brothers. But bring these ten cheeses to the captain of the thousand, and look into the welfare of your brothers and take assurance of them."

David was anxious to go to the army of Israel to see how the soldiers fought the enemy. But when he arrived at the camp he found the men in panic because of Goliath. Upon hearing that no man was willing to challenge the giant, David volunteered to go. Saul heard of this and sent for the young shepherd. When he was questioned, David said to King Saul: "Let not my lord's courage fail him; your servant will go and fight with this Philistine."

"You are not able to go against this Philistine to fight with him," said Saul to David, "for you are but a youth and he has been a warrior from his youth."

"Your servant has been a shepherd with his father's flock," David replied; "and when a lion or a bear would come and take a sheep out of the flock, I would go out after him and attack him and deliver it from his mouth; and if he rose up against me, I would seize him by his beard and wound him and kill him. Your servant has slain both lion and bear." Then David added these courageous words: "The Lord who delivered me from the paw of the lion, and from the paw of the bear, will deliver me from the hand of this Philistine."

Saul was satisfied that David was a valiant fighter. Therefore he had his servants put his heavy armor on David, but the young man felt uncomfortable in such equipment, and he said: "I cannot go with these, for I have not tried them."

Then David took his sling, which he was expert in using, and he went to the brook, where he chose five smooth stones. He put these in his leather bag and started toward the giant. Goliath approached the boy cautiously, for he thought he might be walking into a trap. When he saw young David carrying a sling, he shouted angrily, "Am I a dog that you come to me with sticks?"

Then David said to Goliath:

"You come to me with a sword and a spear and a javelin,
But I come to you in the name of the Lord of hosts,
The God of the battle lines of Israel whom you have taunted.
This day the Lord will deliver you into my hand,

Saul had his servants put his armor on David; but the young man felt uncomfortable in such equipment, and he said: "I cannot go with these, for I have not tried them."

W. WILKE, ARTIST

That I may slay you and sever your head from your body;
And I will this day give your dead body and the dead of
   the camp of the Philistines
To the birds of the air and to the wild beasts of the earth,
That all the earth may know that there is a God in Israel,
And that all this assembly may know
That not with sword and spear does the Lord deliver;
For the battle is the Lord's and He will give you into our hands."

Goliath advanced toward David, towering above the youth in his might. He pushed back his helmet in scorn, and in that moment David was ready to act. Quickly he put a stone in his sling and let it fly with all the strength and skill that he possessed. The stone went straight to its mark; it hit Goliath in the forehead! The giant reeled and fell to the ground. Then David ran forward, grabbed the sword of the giant, and cut off his head. When the Philistines saw their champion lying dead on the battlefield, they fled in terror. The armies of Israel pursued the enemy and defeated them, and David became the hero of his people.

"THANKSGIVING in OLDEN DAYS"

THE traditional Thanksgiving dinner was over at the Barrett home. In fact, Roy and Dick had excused themselves at the first possible moment, realizing that they should work off the "stuffed feeling" in some form of physical exercise.

"Let's get the football and throw some passes to each other," suggested Roy as the brothers stood by the garden gate looking out on the vacant lot.

"Suits me, Roy, provided I can throw a ball after that big dinner," agreed Dick. "I'll get the football. I left it in the garage yesterday."

Soon the oval pigskin was whirling back and forth between the Barrett brothers, and each in his turn raced for it in hot pursuit. Roy shot one pass to his brother that fell some five yards beyond his grasp. "You missed that one, Dick, because you ate too much," jibed Roy.

"Well, Thanksgiving Day comes but once a year," said Dick lamely. "Besides, mother had the best dinner today I believe I ever ate."

"You were extra hungry because we hiked to Bear Lake this morning."

"Anyway, we got some good motion-picture shots of the speedboat races. I can hardly wait until we get them back from processing."

"Didn't you get the roll of films back that you took of us coasting on Seminary Hill?"

"Of course I did, Dick, but I forgot all about them. We were so busy making Thanksgiving baskets and planning the school pageant that the film slipped my mind. I have the package in the desk drawer in my room. Let's take the roll over to Captain Tim's house and see if we can run it on his machine," said Roy, his eyes sparkling with anticipation.

"I want to see the ones I shot of you when you spilled off the toboggan and took a somersault," Dick countered as the two boys entered the back door of their home.

"You get your film," continued Dick, "and I'll see if Bette wants to go with us."

"Perhaps Captain Lane will lend us his projector so the folks can see the pictures tonight," called Roy, bounding up the stairs to his room. The camera was all the equipment Roy possessed as yet. He was hoping to save money so that he could buy a projector before many months passed. In the meantime Captain Lane had invited him to come to his home and use his projector as often as he wished.

It was twilight when Bette, Roy, and Dick rang the Lane doorbell. Mrs. Lane welcomed the trio and led them into the library, where the captain sat reading. "If your Thanksgiving has been as wonderful as ours, you three must be happy," said

W. WILKE, ARTIST

Roy soon sent the pigskin whirling through the air, and Dick awaited it eagerly. It was good exercise after the Thanksgiving dinner, which the Barrett family had enjoyed.

the man, laying his book on the table and waving his young friends toward seats. "Our dinner guests have gone. Mrs. Lane and I have been sitting here in front of the fire thinking of all the good times we've had in the last twenty years."

"Did you have a busy day?" asked Mrs. Lane, picking up her knitting bag by her chair.

"Dick and I hiked to Bear Lake to see the boat races," explained Roy.

"Then all of you were busy eating a big Thanksgiving dinner," put in the captain jovially.

"How right you are. I'll never eat again if I always feel like this," moaned Dick, patting his stomach tenderly.

"I'm glad the Pilgrim Fathers counted their blessings and

set a day to celebrate." Dick was down on the rug trying to take the rubber ball from Chips, who was guarding it jealously. "Probably no other nation has had such a grand reason for thanksgiving as we have."

"Don't think that we are the only people who have lots of blessings," said the captain. "If you go back twenty-five hundred years you'll find a nation holding at least one thanksgiving celebration every year, not only one day but a week at a time."

"Did the children of Israel do that?" asked Roy thoughtfully.

"They did, indeed. Each year the nation celebrated the Feast of Booths, or Tabernacles, in the seventh month. That's about the last of our September or early October. After the nation settled in the land of Canaan the festival was held each year so that the people would remember how God had brought them from the wilderness to their permanent home. So for one week they left their houses and lived in booths."

"Was it a harvest festival?" asked Mrs. Lane, taking an interest in the discussion.

"Yes, my dear, it was the time when the grain and fruits were gathered, and there was joy and feasting everywhere. The people made a pilgrimage to Jerusalem bringing the choice fruit and grain which they had harvested. They built booths in the city streets, in the courtyards, and on top of the flat-roofed houses. They made these booths of palm branches and of myrtle, pine, and olive boughs. The families lived in these booths by day and slept in them at night. The widows, orphans, and strangers were invited to share the feast. We are told that the girls and women often decorated the booths by hanging apples, oranges, nuts, and peppers from the roof."

The Feast of Booths was a joyous occasion, when hundreds of people lived in palm-covered pavilions in the streets of Jerusalem.

W. WILKE, ARTIST

"How exciting that must have been, especially to the boys and girls," said Bette.

"Did they have special programs, Captain Tim?"

"Yes, Dick. The temple was the center of the thanksgiving festival. Every boy and girl, every father and mother, brought some gift as a thank offering. Songs were sung by the Levite choir, and the throng of people joined in the chorus. At these special services old and young waved palm branches like flags or pennants.

"If you had been there the first night you would have seen the temple lighted with many lamps. Early the next morning the priests sounded a long blast on their silver trumpets. The people living in booths replied with glad shouts and welcomed the day of thanksgiving. A priest brought a jar of water from Brook Kidron and poured it into a silver basin in the courtyard of the temple. This water represented the fountain that gushed out when Moses struck the rock at the Lord's command. You remember how by the miracle God gave thirsty Israel water to drink in the desert."

"Was this the only festival the children of Israel celebrated?" asked Dick.

"No, there were other feasts," captain Tim replied.

"Don't you remember the Passover Feast?" Bette reminded her brother.

"That was in honor of the nation's escape from Egypt at the time of the Exodus."

"That's right, Bette. And in addition to that great day each year, there was also the Feast of Pentecost, when the nation celebrated the end of the wheat harvest," added the man.

"If they had continued to thank the heavenly Father for His blessings they would have remained a great nation. When they forgot the Lord they turned to worship idols. Then they went into captivity, and eventually their nation was overthrown."

"I remember a verse in the Psalms my grandmother used to repeat to me: 'Bless the Lord, O my soul, and forget not all His benefits.'" Mrs. Lane repeated the words softly as she watched the crackling logs in the fireplace.

"'And forget not all His benefits,'" repeated Captain Tim. "What a lesson for us when we have so much to be thankful for."

"We had a special reason for bothering you this evening, Captain Tim," ventured Roy after everyone had waited quietly a few moments. "We hoped we could see the film I took during the snowstorm a few weeks ago."

"Roy shot some pictures of coasting," explained Bette eagerly, "so we are all anxious to see them."

"Nothing would please us more, would it, my dear?" The captain turned to his wife as he spoke.

"It would be the ideal ending for a perfect day, Timothy."

Willing young hands set up the screen while Captain Lane made ready the projector. "After we run your film, perhaps you'd like to see some pictures I took in Palestine that I have never shown you," suggested the man. "I found them in a box in the attic last week. It's a reel on the life of the shepherds of the East. I call it, 'The Twenty-Third Psalm in Pictures.'"

"You always have a treat for us," Bette declared.

"How right you are," agreed Dick, as the first pictures of a snowball fight flashed on the silver screen.

4

DAVID FLEES From SAUL

1 SAMUEL 18:1 to 20:42

WHEN David returned from his victorious fight with Goliath, the Philistine giant, Saul took him to the royal court. The king would not permit this youth to return to his home at Bethlehem when he could be a valuable leader in the army. David was given command of a thousand soldiers, and he played sweet music on his harp when the king was sad and despondent.

King Saul became jealous of David, however, for he saw that the people loved this young hero. When the king and the shepherd returned from the battle, the women welcomed them by singing:

> "Saul has slain his thousands,
> But David his ten thousands."

As David's popularity increased, the king became furious. One day while the youth was playing for Saul, the angry monarch seized his spear and hurled it at the harp player, saying, "I will pin David to the wall." But the young man escaped from the mad king, for God was with him.

While living at Saul's court, David became acquainted with Jonathan, Saul's son. The young men loved each other and be-

(51)

On the second day of the feast King Saul asked:
"Why has not the son of Jesse come to the meal?"

came true friends. Grieved because his father hated David, Jonathan determined to shield his new-found friend from danger.

Now Michal, Saul's younger daughter, fell in love with David, and the king consented to the marriage, provided the young man would go out to battle and destroy a hundred Philistines. By this cunning plan Saul thought that the enemy would kill David. But the Lord protected the valiant young warrior, and he slew two hundred Philistines in battle. Now the king had to keep his promise. He gave Michal to David to be his wife, and she loved him dearly.

Saul was more determined than ever to destroy his son-in-law. Again the king threw his spear at David in an attempt to kill him, but once more the youth escaped and fled to his own house. Saul sent spies to David's home with instructions to kill him when he came out in the morning. But Michal heard of the plot and made a plan to save her husband. "If you do not make your escape tonight," she warned, "tomorrow you will be a corpse." So in the darkness Michal let David down from a window, and he sought refuge in Samuel's house at Ramah.

Soon after this, Saul sent an assurance to David that he would make peace with the youth; but David did not have faith in the king's word. David met Jonathan secretly and said to him: "What have I done; what is my guilt; and what is my sin before your father, that he is seeking my life?"

Jonathan tried to convince David that the king would not kill him.

"Nevertheless as surely as the Lord lives," exclaimed David, "and as you live, there is but a step between me and death."

Then the two friends made a plan. A sacred festival was to

As the lad ran across the field at his bidding, Jonathan shot an arrow beyond him and shouted: "Is not the arrow beyond you? Make haste, be quick, do not stand still!"

be held the following day, and David and Jonathan were expected to enjoy the feast at the king's table. David was afraid to appear, however, because of Saul's treachery. Therefore the two friends decided that Jonathan should go to the feast and David would hide in a field near the king's banquet hall. If Saul asked where David was, Jonathan would say that he had gone to Bethlehem to visit his family. If the king would say, "Good," and seem to be pleased, David could be sure that it was safe for him to return to the court. If the king was angry, however, they would know that the old jealousy still burned in his heart.

Jonathan went to the king's hall, and on the first day of the feast Saul did not ask about David. However, on the second day, when he saw the seat still vacant, he said, "Why has not the son of Jesse come to the meal, either yesterday or today?"

Jonathan explained to his father, saying: "David urgently asked leave of me to go to Bethlehem, for he said, 'Let me go, I pray you, since our family has a sacrifice in the city; and my brothers have commanded me. Now if I have found favor in your sight, let me slip away, I pray you, and see my brothers.' Therefore he has not come to the king's table."

When Saul heard these words, his anger flamed against Jonathan, and he picked up his spear and threw it at his own son. Jonathan dodged out of the way, however, and on the third morning went out into the field, accompanied by a small boy.

Jonathan said to the boy: "Run, find now the arrows that I am about to shoot."

As the lad ran, Jonathan shot an arrow beyond him and shouted: "Is not the arrow beyond you? Make haste, be quick, do not stand still!"

Quickly the boy gathered up the arrows and brought them back to Jonathan. Then the man commanded the boy to carry the bow and arrows into the town. The boy went on his way not knowing that the shooting of the arrows had been a signal for David to flee from Saul. But before the shepherd of Bethlehem departed, he came out of his hiding place behind a heap of stones and said good-by to his friend. Afterward Jonathan returned to the king's court, but David fled for his life—a fugitive from King Saul.

5

DAVID and HIS MIGHTY MEN

1 SAMUEL 21:1 to 24:22

DAVID felt lonely and forsaken after he left Jonathan. Where should he go? What should he do? He knew he was an outcast, a man hunted by the king's soldiers. Scarcely realizing where he was going, David made his way along the road that led to the city of Nob. It was in that town that the tent of meeting had been set up after the golden ark was taken by the Philistines.

Making his way to the tent of meeting, David met Ahimelech, the high priest. The man of God trembled when he saw David, for he recognized that this was the brave warrior who had killed the giant Goliath. The priest remembered, too, that the giant's sword, a trophy of the great victory that had been won over the enemy, was in the tent of meeting. David asked Ahimelech for food, but he did not reveal to the high priest that he was trying to escape from King Saul.

"There is no ordinary bread in my possession," said Ahimelech, "but there is holy bread." The priest gave David the hallowed bread from the golden table in the holy place. Since the fugitive was without weapons, he asked the aged priest: "Is there not here in your possession a spear or a sword?"

"The sword of Goliath the Philistine, whom you slew in the

Valley of Elah, see, it is wrapped in a garment behind the ephod," said the priest. "If you wish to take that, take it, for there is no other except that here."

"There is none like it, give it to me," said David.

Ahimelech had no idea that he was helping an enemy of the king. He knew David was Saul's armor-bearer, therefore he thought he was pleasing the monarch when he gave this young warrior food and a sword and helped him on his journey. Now, Doeg, the royal shepherd, happened to be in the tent of meeting, and he saw what the priest had given David. He immediately carried the news to Saul, and we shall soon see how this sealed the doom of the priests of Nob.

David pushed on toward the southwest and finally reached the Cave of Adullam. Soon his father and brothers came to the cave. They were afraid that Saul would try to kill them because of his hatred for David. The brave warrior arranged for his family to live with the king of Moab in the land where his great-grandmother Ruth was born.

Since David was an outlaw, other men began flocking to him for protection. They offered him their allegiance, for they knew that Saul was a wicked king. Soon the Cave of Adullam was the camp for about four hundred men who were loyal to their leader.

Word that David was hiding in a cave reached Saul, and he made plans at once to surround it and kill the fugitive. But David heard of the king's plan and led his band of men to new hiding places where they could not be trapped by the royal army.

When Saul heard that Ahimelech, the high priest, had given food and a sword to David, he commanded that all the priests of Nob should be killed. The aged priest of the Lord tried to ex-

"The sword of Goliath. . . . whom you slew in the Valley of Elah, see, it is wrapped in a garment behind the Ephod," said Ahimelech. "If you wish to take that, take it."

plain to the monarch that he was innocent, but wicked Saul would not listen to reason. All the priests were massacred except Abiathar, a son of Ahimelech. He escaped to David and told him what had happened. David remembered how he had deceived the high priest, and he was sorry for his terrible mistake. He said to Abiathar: "I knew that day, because Doeg the Edomite was there, that he would surely tell Saul. I myself am responsible for all the lives of your father's house. Remain with me, fear not; for he that seeks my life seeks your life, for you shall be a charge to me."

Still hunted by King Saul, David found no safe place to hide. He heard that the Philistines had attacked the Israelites at Keilah, so he led his warriors against the enemy and saved the

town from ruin. However, the king of Israel was in hot pursuit, so David hurried his men into the wild regions of Ziph, where they were safe for the moment. In this lonely wilderness Jonathan found his friend and cheered him with words of courage. He said: "Fear not, for the hand of Saul my father shall not find you, and you shall be king over Israel and I shall be next to you; and that too my father Saul well knows." At this time we see that Jonathan loved his friend so much that he was willing to give up his claim to the throne of Israel in order that David, who had been chosen by the Lord, might be the ruler.

When Saul heard that David was in the desert of Engedi, he led his army of three thousand men in search of him. As the warriors were climbing the mountains, King Saul entered a cave to rest. Now, who should be hiding in that cave but David and his soldiers! Of course David's men urged him to kill his enemy, but the young leader refused. He said he would not kill the man whom the Lord had anointed king. He did, however, steal up to Saul while he rested and cut off a part of the king's robe.

After Saul had departed from the cave, David called to him saying: "Why do you listen to the words of the men who said, 'See, David seeks your hurt?' Behold, this day your eyes see that the Lord gave you into my hand in the cave, but I refused to kill you and had pity on you."

Saul looked at his robe and saw that a piece had been cut from it. Then David said: "The Lord judge between me and you, and the Lord avenge me of you; but my hand shall not be upon you."

When David had finished speaking, Saul said: "Is this your voice, my son David?"

David's men urged him to kill his enemy, but he refused. He did, however, steal up to him while Saul rested, and cut off a part of his robe.

W. WILKE, ARTIST

When three of his men brought him water from Bethlehem, David realized the danger they had faced to get it. He would not drink it, but poured it on the ground.

Then Saul lifted up his voice and wept. He said to David: "You are more righteous than I, for you have shown me kindness, while I have shown you evil."

Then Saul and David made peace, and the king returned to his home.

David now had a band of "mighty men" who were daring fighters. Some of their heroic deeds are recorded in the Bible. They were completely loyal to their leader. Once while David was far from his home, his men heard him say: "Oh that someone would give me a drink of water from the well of Bethlehem that is at the gate!"

Three of his men slipped away from the camp, went through the enemy lines, and got a pitcher of water from that well. When they brought the water to David and he realized the grave danger they had faced to get it, he would not drink it, but poured it on the ground as an offering to the Lord.

SAUL'S LAST BATTLE

1 SAMUEL 28:3 to 2 SAMUEL 1:27

KING SAUL and the whole na-
tion mourned when Samuel died, for the prophet had been a
mighty leader in Israel. From the day that his mother, Hannah,
had brought him to the tent of meeting, he had obeyed the Lord
and served Him faithfully. He had been a good judge, urging
the people to do right.

The king felt alone and forsaken as he faced the fierce armies
of the Philistines encamped on the plain of Jezreel, the place
where Gideon had once fought victoriously with his three hundred men. Saul wished he could talk with Samuel so he might
know what to do to save the nation. But now the prophet was
dead, and the Lord would not speak to the rejected ruler.

Saul remembered that there were witches in the land, people
who claimed to make the dead speak. The Lord had commanded that all witches and spirit mediums should be destroyed,
and King Saul had tried to do this. Now, however, he desired
to find one who might help him talk to Samuel.

The king's servants reported there was a woman at En-dor
who could reveal secrets. Of course the witch could not bring
the dead who sleep in their graves back to life, but she could
deceive Saul.

(63)

5—K. Q.

Disguised as common soldiers, the king and two of his guards made their way by night to the witch's hiding place in a cave at En-dor. The woman was afraid when she saw the three visitors, but the king immediately promised her safety. The woman asked: "Whom shall I bring up to you?"

"Bring Samuel up for me," requested Saul.

When a ghostlike figure appeared, the woman screamed and said: "Why have you deceived me, for you are Saul?"

"Do not be alarmed," said the king. "What have you seen?"

The woman declared she had seen an old man coming up out of the earth. It was not Samuel, but an evil spirit, and it brought a warning of defeat and death to Saul. The king fell to the ground weak and frightened, and his servants were afraid that he would die. The witch prepared some food, and after the king had rested and eaten he was able to return to his army.

The next morning the armies of Israel and the hordes of the Philistines clashed on the plains of Shunem. The princes of the Philistines pushed forward so fiercely that the men of Israel could not stop them. Finally the soldiers of King Saul broke and ran, and the Philistines pushed forward and overtook Saul and his sons. Jonathan and his two brothers were killed, and the king was wounded. When Saul saw that the enemy would cap-ture him, he fell on his own sword and died.

David and his warriors had not fought in this battle. They were camped at Ziklag when a messenger from the king's army came to tell David the news. When the man bowed before David, the brave warrior said: "From where do you come?"

"From the camp of Israel I have escaped," he replied.

"What is the situation? I pray you, tell me," said David.

The Philistine army pushed forward and overtook Saul. Jonathan and his two brothers were slain, and Saul was wounded. The king fell on his own sword and died.

"The people," said the messenger, "fled from the battle, and many of the people have fallen, and also Saul and Jonathan his son are dead."

Then David took hold of his garments and tore them, and all the men who were with him did likewise. This was the customary way for the people to show their sorrow. David and his men fasted and wept until evening. Memories of his deep friendship with Jonathan came to David's mind. Taking his harp, the man who had comforted Saul with beautiful music now sang a beautiful lament for the loss of the king and of Jonathan. The song ended with these beautiful lines:

> "Saul and Jonathan, beloved and lovely!
> In life and in death they were not divided;

Swifter than eagles were they,
They were stronger than lions.

"O daughters of Israel, weep over Saul,
Who clothed you in scarlet daintily,
Who adorned your garments with gold and jewels;
How are the mighty fallen in the midst of battle!

"O Jonathan! by your death am I mortally wounded,
I am distressed for you, my brother Jonathan!
You were exceedingly dear to me,
Your love was more marvelous to me than the
    love of women.

"How have the mighty fallen,
And the weapons of war perished!"

Memory Verses

"Samuel said, Hath the Lord as great delight in burnt offerings and sacrifices, as in obeying the voice of the Lord? Behold, to obey is better than sacrifice, and to hearken than the fat of rams." 1 Samuel 15:22.

"The Lord said unto Samuel, Look not on his countenance, or on the height of his stature; because I have refused him: for the Lord seeth not as man seeth; for man looketh on the outward appearance, but the Lord looketh on the heart." 1 Samuel 16:7.

"David said moreover, The Lord that delivered me out of the paw of the lion, and out of the paw of the bear, He will deliver me out of the hand of this Philistine. And Saul said unto David, Go, and the Lord be with thee." 1 Samuel 17:37

"Then said David to the Philistine, Thou comest to me with a sword, and with a spear, and with a shield: but I come to thee in the name of the Lord of hosts, the God of the armies of Israel, whom thou hast defied. . . . And all this assembly shall know that the Lord saveth not with sword and spear: for the battle is the Lord's, and He will give you into our hands." 1 Samuel 17:45-47.

"Saul and Jonathan were lovely and pleasant in their lives, and in their death they were not divided: they were swifter than eagles, they were stronger than lions." 2 Samuel 1:23.

SHEPHERDS of PALESTINE

"WHAT do you think of sheep rais-
ing?" asked Captain Lane of the three Barretts as they drove
down the narrow road leading from the Ridgeway sheep ranch
to the highway.

"It looks like a lot of hard work to me," commented Dick,
thinking of the shearing, dipping, and constant attention that
a flock of sheep required.

"I'd like taking care of the lambs in the spring," said Bette.
"Jane Ridgeway told me how she cared for a baby lamb when
its mother would not claim it. The tiny ones are fed with a
bottle like a baby."

"They seem to be sort of dumb, Captain Tim. Do you remember that Mr. Ridgeway said that sheep would follow their
leader no matter if it took them to their death? I guess they
don't do much thinking for themselves." Roy was sitting by
the captain in the front seat of the car and smiled broadly at
the man as he spoke.

"That makes them like some humans, don't you think, Roy?"

Riding out into the country on a crisp November day is
fun, particularly when it is a holiday for three wide-awake
juniors. On this morning, the Friday after Thanksgiving, Cap-

(69)

"What do you think of sheep raising?" asked
Captain Lane of the three young Barretts as
the visitors left the Ridgeway sheep ranch.

W. WILKE, ARTIST

tain Lane had urged Bette, Roy, and Dick to keep him company as he drove to the Ridgeway ranch some twenty-five miles from the city. After an hour of tramping across the rolling hills of the ranch to look at flocks of sheep, it was cozy to be back in the warm car once more.

"Here's hoping I got some good pictures of that sheep dog rounding up the flock." Roy had taken his motion-picture camera with him on this sunny morning to take some shots on the sheep ranch.

"King is certainly a wonderful dog. The way he rounded up the sheep was almost human." Bette loved dogs, particularly Chips, the captain's cocker spaniel.

"I'd say that it was more than human," returned Dick. "I'd like to see any of us go chasing after them across the pasture and get the same results."

"Farmer Barlow says I should have a flock of sheep grazing on the back pasture at Hillcrest farm. I thought I'd drive out here today to see about buying some," the man explained.

"Sheepherding is different in the Orient, isn't it, captain?" asked Roy.

"It must be," agreed Dick, "for in the moving pictures Captain Tim showed us last night the shepherd seems to live with his flock most of the time."

"You're right, Dick," replied the captain. "I've seen shepherds on the hills near Bethlehem caring for their flocks the same way David did three thousand years ago, the same way shepherds did the night angels announced the birth of Jesus."

"In your pictures it seemed that the shepherds were boys," said Bette.

THREE LIONS

The shepherd boy of Palestine still carries a sling such as young David used. It is made by cutting a tuft of long wool from the back of a sheep and spinning it into yarn.

"That's true," Captain Lane agreed. "The youngest son in the family is usually the shepherd. That is, of course, if he is old enough to take any responsibility at all. He wears a simple robe of cotton held by a leather belt. He also has an outer coat which protects him from rain and chilly nights."

"What weapon does he carry to protect him if his sheep are attacked by wild beasts?" asked Dick.

"You wouldn't call his equipment much protection. He carries a rod, which is a light stick with a hooklike end. This helps the shepherd to help his sheep over rough stones or to pull them out of ravines if they are trapped. He also has a rod which is like a cane. These are two weapons. Oh, yes, there is one more —the sling, which the shepherd makes by cutting a tuft of long wool from the back of a sheep and spinning it into yarn. A web is formed to hold the stone, and the ends are braided into a cord about three feet long."

"Is that the kind of sling David used to kill Goliath?" Dick questioned eagerly.

"No doubt that's the sling, Dick. I've seen shepherds so skilled with their shots they could sling a stone flying toward a savage wolf and send him scurrying away into the woods. The shepherds practice slinging for hours at a time. The Bible tells about some left-handed men of the tribe of Benjamin who 'could sling stones at an hairbreadth, and not miss.' That's real accuracy."

The captain took his foot off the accelerator, and the car slowed down. They were approaching a stop sign at the junction of two highways.

"David surely loved his sheep," said Bette. "He must have thought of them when he wrote the twenty-third psalm."

"Have you ever considered those verses of poetry in connection with the shepherds of Palestine, Captain Tim?" asked Roy.

The car was speeding ahead once more toward the city, and Captain Lane resumed his conversation.

"Yes, one of the most interesting experiences I had in Bethlehem was hearing an old shepherd explain the meaning of every line of the Shepherd Psalm. He said the good shepherd leads his sheep into the valley where there is plenty of grass.

RAAD, THREE LIONS

An Oriental shepherd brings home a lost sheep, carrying it gently and treating it kindly.
Captain Tim reminded his young friends of the Good Shepherd and His love for us.

That makes one think of the setting, 'The Lord is my Shepherd; I shall not want.'

"During the heat of the summer day the man or boy, whichever it is, takes the sheep to a cool, shady meadow so they may lie down and rest."

"That reminds one of the line, 'He maketh me to lie down in green pastures,'" put in Dick Barrett.

"Exactly," continued the driver of the car. "And when the sheep are cool, the shepherd takes them to the brook to drink. He never drives his sheep, as they do in Western countries. The

Oriental shepherd always leads them. He knows every one of the sheep and calls them all by name. We have David's words: 'He leadeth me beside the still waters. He restoreth my soul.' The still waters are quiet pools or wells where the flock can drink safely. If they were caught in swift water they would be swept away, since they become very heavy when their wool soaks up water.

"When evening comes, the shepherd leads his flock to shelter. He knows the safe paths where the sheep will be safe from enemies. That must be what David meant when he wrote: 'He leadeth me in the paths of righteousness for His name's sake.'

"It isn't easy to lead sheep in right paths unless the shepherd knows the country. He may take them along a stony path which leads to a precipice. No matter where he goes he leads his sheep. Perhaps darkness comes as the flock enters a narrow gorge. The shepherd talks to his sheep and they hear him tap, tap on the rocks with his staff."

"Captain Tim, don't you suppose David is describing that experience in the verses in the psalm which talk of the valley of the shadow?" asked Roy.

" 'Yea, though I walk through the valley of the shadow of death, I will fear no evil: for Thou art with me; Thy rod and Thy staff they comfort me.' " Bette repeated the words without a mistake, for she knew the Shepherd Psalm by heart and she loved every word of it.

"One day I watched a flock of sheep following the shepherd. Some of them would fall behind the main flock to nibble tufts of grass," the captain continued. "The shepherd would call, and there would be a patter of feet as the sheep hurried to him.

"It isn't easy to lead sheep in right paths unless the shepherd knows the country," explained Captain Lane to his young friends. "No matter where he goes he leads his sheep."

"Perhaps the sheep have a meager pasture in the afternoon, so in the evening the shepherd feeds them with grain from his little storehouse."

"That would fit the next verse," Dick said quickly. " 'Thou preparest a table before me in the presence of mine enemies.' I suppose that when lions and wolves roamed outside the sheepfold, the shepherd guarded his flock from harm."

"You are right, Dick," the man answered, taking his eyes from the highway for a moment to glance at his friend.

"Finish the story, captain. It isn't complete yet," urged Bette.

"Always anxious for more, aren't you, young lady?" teased

the man. "Well, the next morning the shepherd inspects his flock one by one. If a sheep has been scratched by a rock or a thornbush, the shepherd puts oil on the sore. We are told that sometimes snakes pop out of their holes in the rocks and bite the sheep on the nose. The shepherd has special ointment to help heal these snakebites. After the sheep are inspected, the shepherd takes them to a stone trough, where they drink. The shepherd draws the water from the well and pours it into the trough so rapidly it overflows before the sheep can drink it. That's David's picture when he says: 'Thou anointest my head with oil; my cup runneth over. Surely goodness and mercy shall follow me all the days of my life: and I will dwell in the house of the Lord forever.' "

"What a picture of shepherd life!" Dick spoke thoughtfully as he reviewed the words of the psalm.

"Jesus is the Good Shepherd who loves the sheep. Do you remember how He pictured the ninety-nine sheep safe in the sheepfold? The shepherd left them and went out into the stormy night to find the one lost sheep. That is how much God loves us." The captain spoke softly and began to hum the tune of "The Ninety and Nine."

"If we are lost sheep we should know enough to go home, Captain Tim," said Bette in a practical turn of mind.

"We should, all right, I agree; but some folks don't realize they are lost and don't want to go home to the Father."

"Remember the time we got lost in the woods, Dick?" asked Roy, turning to his brother, who was sitting in the back seat with Bette.

"Boy, will I ever forget that night!"

"It's bad enough to be lost," commented the man. "But it's worse to be lost and not know it."

"I guess that's true. I never thought of it that way before," Roy admitted. "To be lost and think you're going the right way would be pretty bad, indeed. Here we are at the city park. We've made good time, Captain Tim."

Soon the car was pulling to the curb on Maple Street in front of the Barrett home. Three carefree juniors jumped from the automobile and showered Thank you's on their friend. "When you get those sheep, Captain Tim, we'll help you shear them," called Dick as the car pulled away from the curb.

7

DAVID IS CROWNED KING

2 SAMUEL 2:1 to 6:23

THE death of Saul made it possible for David to return in safety to his own country. He knew that God had chosen him to be ruler of Israel after Saul, but he was not certain what he should do to win the people to him. The Lord instructed David to go to Hebron, the chief city of Judah.

When David marched into Hebron with six hundred warriors and their families and possessions, he was joyfully welcomed by the men of the city. Since David was from the tribe of Judah, the men of that tribe were proud to have him rule over them, and they anointed him king.

Now David's kingship had scarcely been announced when Abner, commander of Saul's army, proclaimed that Ish-bosheth, Saul's son, was king. This rival ruler made his headquarters at Mahanaim, a town on the east side of Jordan. For more than two years there were two rulers in Israel. Quarreling broke out among Saul's men, and Abner was killed. Soon afterward Ish-bosheth was murdered by his own guards. Then at last, all of the tribes of Israel came to David in Hebron and proclaimed him their king.

On the coronation day what memories must have come to David! He remembered the long years of hardship and danger

(79)

Priests, soldiers, and leaders from all the tribes were present when the son of Jesse, in royal robes, knelt and the crown was placed on his head.

W. WILKE, ARTIST

he had suffered since the time he had been called from sheepherding to be anointed by Samuel. Now, at thirty years of age,
David stood before the vast throng of his people. Priests, soldiers, and leaders from all the tribes were present when the son
of Jesse, in royal robes, knelt before the vast assembly and the
crown was placed on his head.

It was time to choose a capital city near the center of the
kingdom. After studying the situation, David selected the
mountain city of Jerusalem, a stronghold of the Jebusites which
the armies of Israel had never conquered. The king led his soldiers against the fortress, and they captured it. Thus Jerusalem
became the city of David, and here the king built his palace.

Once more the Philistines came against Israel in the Valley
of Rephaim, only a short distance from Jerusalem. David asked
the Lord what he should do in this emergency. "Shall I go up
against the Philistines? Wilt Thou deliver them into my hand?"
he prayed.

The Lord gave the king instructions to go against the enemy,
and the promise was given that Israel would have the victory.

The king led his valiant soldiers against the enemy and defeated them, but this did not discourage the Philistines. Once
more they came up against Israel, and again David asked the
Lord what he should do. This time he was told: "You shall not
go up; go around to their rear and come upon them opposite
the balsam trees. Then when you hear the sound of marching
in the tops of the balsam trees, make haste, for at that moment
the Lord has gone forth before you to fall upon the camp of the
Philistines."

David did as the Lord commanded, and the enemy was de-

As the cart was moving along the rough road, one of the oxen stumbled, and the ark tottered and wobbled so much it almost fell. Uzzah reached out to steady the ark.

feated and driven out of the land of Israel. Never again during the reign of David did the Philistines trouble the people of Israel.

As peace came to the country, the king was determined to bring the golden ark to Jerusalem. It had remained in the house of Abinadab since the day the Philistines had sent it back to Israel on an oxcart. The king summoned thirty thousand leaders from the twelve tribes to join him in the royal procession. They marched to the house of Abinadab at Kirjath-jearim, nine miles from Jerusalem. The ark was placed on a new cart drawn by oxen, and the people followed, singing songs and playing musical instruments.

As the cart was moving along the rough road, one of the oxen stumbled, and the ark tottered and wobbled so much it looked as if it might fall off. Uzzah, who was walking beside the cart, reached out to steady the ark. "Then the anger of the Lord blazed against Uzzah and God struck him down there because he put his hand to the ark and there he died beside the ark of God."

Long before this, God had given instructions that no one except the priests should carry or touch the sacred ark. If David had followed the Lord's command, the ark would have been carried as it had been in the days of Moses, and this divine judgment would not have fallen on Uzzah.

The people were afraid because of the sudden death of this man, so the king left the golden ark in the house of a farmer, Obed-edom, and the procession returned to Jerusalem.

Three months later the king called the leaders together. With priests to perform the sacred work of carrying the ark, the procession marched to Jerusalem, where a special service of thanksgiving was planned. The golden ark was placed in the tent which David had prepared, and the people blessed the name of the Lord. Then the king gave each visitor a loaf of bread, a piece of meat, and a cake of raisins, and every man departed for his home, rejoicing that he had such a good king to rule over Israel.

Captain Tim's Bible Quiz

Dick Barrett had finished his class assignments one evening and decided to see how much he remembered about the lives of Saul and David. When he finished writing down his brain teasers he had this list of questions. Can you answer all twenty of them? The correct answers are found on page 251.

1. What was the name of Saul's father?
2. In what town did David live when he was a child?
3. What shout did the people give when Saul was made king that is still used at coronations today?
4. Who was the famous general of Saul's army?
5. What was the name of the Philistine giant that David killed?
6. What did Ahimelech the priest give David to eat when he was hungry?
7. From what tribe did Saul's family come?
8. What weapon did David receive from the high priest when he was fleeing from Saul?
9. Where did Saul go to seek counsel of a witch?
10. What city did David choose as the capital of Israel?
11. Where was David made king of Israel?
12. What man was killed for touching the golden ark?
13. What was the name of Saul's daughter who married David?
14. Which of David's songs is known as the Shepherd Psalm?
15. Who was the heathen king that Saul spared when he was commanded to destroy an entire nation?
16. Who was David's friend that he loved with all his heart?
17. What did David's men once bring to him from his home in Bethlehem?
18. When Saul's mind was troubled, how did David comfort him?
19. In what town did the prophet Samuel live?
20. What was the harvest festival in which Israel gave thanks to God for all their blessings?

8

A KINDNESS and a CRIME

2 SAMUEL 9:1 to 12:23

THE memory of his close friendship with Jonathan lingered in King David's mind. He wanted to do a kind deed to a member of Saul's family as a token of his enduring love. One day the king said: "Is there anyone left of the family of Saul to whom I may show kindness for Jonathan's sake?"

Royal servants soon found a servant named Ziba who had been in Saul's palace. When he was brought before David, he said: "There is a son of Jonathan still living, who is crippled in his feet."

And the king said: "Where is he?"

Ziba told David that Mephibosheth, the son of Jonathan, lived at Lo-debar. The king sent for him at once; but when the crippled man came to the royal court, he was fearful. Perhaps he thought that David would kill him because he was a grandson of Saul.

"Fear not," said David to him, "for I will surely show you kindness for the sake of Jonathan your father and I will restore to you the entire estate of Saul your grandfather, and you shall always eat bread at my table."

Such kindness was more than Mephibosheth could have ever

(85)

"Fear not," said David to Mephibosheth,
"for I will surely show you kindness
for the sake of Jonathan your father."

W. WILKE, ARTIST

The prophet looked at the king of Israel and said: "You are the man!" He went on to reveal David's sin: "You have slain Uriah the Hittite, and you have taken his wife."

expected. He dwelt in the king's palace and ate at David's table like one of his sons.

For many years David served Israel faithfully, and he loved the Lord of heaven. After he had built his palace at Jerusalem, however, he committed a crime. He thought that it was kept secret from men; but God who sees all that we do, had made a record of it. The day came when the Lord gave Nathan, the prophet, a message for David. The prophet came before the king and revealed the terrible sin by telling a story. This was Nathan's parable:

"There were two men in a certain city, the one rich, and the other poor. The rich man owned very many flocks and herds. But the poor man had nothing but a single little ewe lamb, which he had bought. He reared it and it grew up with him and with his children. It would eat from his food and drink from his cup, and it lay in his bosom, and it was like a daughter to him. Now there came a traveler to the rich man, and he refused to take from his own flock or his own herd to make ready for the wayfarer who had come to him, but he took the poor man's lamb and prepared it for the man who had come to him."

The king was very angry when he heard the prophet's story, and he said: "As the Lord lives, the man that does this is worthy of death; he shall restore the lamb sevenfold, because he did this and because he showed no pity."

The prophet looked at the king of Israel and said: "You are the man!" Then he went on to reveal David's sin by telling him that God said: "You have slain Uriah the Hittite with the sword, and you have taken his wife to be your wife, having slain him with the sword of the Ammonites. Now therefore the sword shall never depart from your house, because you have despised Me and have taken the wife of Uriah the Hittite to be your wife."

Soon all the nation learned that David had killed an innocent man. David had fallen in love with Bath-sheba, the beautiful wife of Uriah, and he had wanted her for his own wife. The king had sent a message to Joab, the general of his army, who had been fighting a battle against Israel's enemies. In the letter David had told the general to put the brave soldier Uriah in the front lines and then withdraw his forces so that the man would be trapped and killed. The general had obeyed, and Uriah had died in battle.

When David married Bath-sheba, he thought that no one would ever know he had caused Uriah to be slain. But now the prophet of God stood before the king, revealing that he was a murderer.

With humble, sorrowful heart David said: "I have sinned against the Lord."

"The Lord has also taken away your sin; you shall not die," the prophet replied. How wonderful it is to have our wrongs forgiven so that they will not be held against us!

A son was born to David and Bath-sheba, but he became very sick. The king was worried, and he prayed that the child might live. Now the prophet Nathan told the king that because he had sinned, his prayer would not be answered. The little son died; but the sorrowing king repented of his evil way, and God forgave him.

9

ABSALOM, a REBELLIOUS SON

2 SAMUEL 15:1 to 19:5

TROUBLE arose in David's family, and there was strife between the king and his sons, and among the sons themselves. David had failed to teach his children to obey, and when they did wrong he was afraid to punish them, probably because he was weak himself.

Absalom, one of David's sons, was a handsome prince. He was proud of his thick, beautiful hair. In fact, it was so heavy that he trimmed off more than three pounds of hair when he cut it each year.

The young prince was selfish and headstrong. He quarreled with his brothers and dreamed of the day when he might be king. He became impatient, however; and as his ambition grew, he decided that he would steal the throne from his father.

Proud Absalom rode about Jerusalem in a chariot drawn by fine horses, while fifty men ran before him to clear the streets. Soon the prince became a popular hero, followed by many people. He was clever and crafty, too, for he would rise up early in the morning and go to the city gate where the men entered who desired to see the king. Absalom would stop the travelers, listen to their stories, and pretend to sympathize with them in their trouble. Then he would say slyly: "O that someone would make me a judge in the land, that any man who had a suit or cause might come to me, that I might give him justice!" Whenever a man would bow before him, the prince would put out his hand and take hold of him and kiss him. In this way Absalom won the hearts of many people in Israel.

Now, David did not know that his son was trying to take the throne from him. However, the day came when Absalom decided to act. He sent messengers to the leaders of the twelve tribes, calling on them to revolt against King David. Then the prince went to his father and deceived him by saying: "Let me go, I pray you, and pay my vow, which I vowed to the Lord, in Hebron."

"Go in peace," said the king.

Now Absalom went to Hebron for the purpose of gathering his army. The next thing David knew, a messenger came to the palace saying that the rebellious son had made himself king.

When David heard the fearful news, he was frightened and said: "Up and away; for otherwise there will be for us no escape from Absalom. Make haste to be off, lest he quickly overtake us and set evil in motion against us and put the city to the sword."

Ittai, a loyal friend from the Philistines, joined David, bringing six hundred warriors with him. The king left Jerusalem hurriedly with his faithful followers. As he climbed the road leading over Mount Olivet, he wept. His head was covered as a sign of mourning, and he walked barefoot to show his disgrace. Through the night the king's company fled eastward, making their way down the rocky, desolate slopes to the Jordan River. Ziba, Mephibosheth's servant, brought food for the fugitives and mules for the king to ride on.

W. WILKE, ARTIST

As King David left Jerusalem and climbed the road leading over Mount Olivet, he wept. His head was covered as a sign of mourning, and he was barefoot to show his disgrace.

Hushai, a trusted counselor of King David, joined the royal party as it left the city; but the king sent this friend back to the palace, and when Absalom captured Jerusalem without a struggle, Hushai pretended to support the rebel cause. This pleased the prince, and he listened to Hushai's advice. Absalom had planned to send an army at once in pursuit of his father, but Hushai determined to delay action so that the king would have time to gather his warriors and fight.

"You know your father and his men," said Hushai to Absalom, "that they are tried warriors and thoroughly aroused, like a bear in the open robbed of her cubs. Furthermore your father is an expert campaigner and will not spend the night with the people. Even now he has hidden himself in one of the caves or in some other place. In case he falls upon the people at the first, whoever hears a report will say, 'There has been a slaughter among the people who follow Absalom.' Then even the valiant man whose heart is like the heart of a lion, will utterly lose courage; for all Israel knows that your father is a skilled warrior, and those who are with him are valiant men. But I counsel that all Israel be surely gathered together to you, from Dan to Beersheba, as many as the sand that is by the sea, with you yourself marching in their midst. Thus we will come upon him in some place where he has been located, and we will light upon him as the dew falls upon the ground; and of him and of all the men who are with him there shall not be left even one. But if he withdraws into a city, then all Israel will bring ropes to that city and we will drag it into the valley, until not even a pebble can be found there."

Absalom liked this counsel and accepted it. Then Hushai sent a secret message to David telling him to cross the Jordan River with his loyal followers and seek safety in a walled city.

David made plans with Joab, his general, to divide the small loyal army into three groups in order to fight Absalom's forces. The king loved his son in spite of his rebellion, and when a battle was about to be fought David gave instructions to his officers, saying: "Deal gently for my sake with the young man, with Absalom!"

The fight took place in the woods, and David's warriors won a great victory. Absalom was riding through the forest on a mule when he met some of David's men. The prince probably turned to flee, and as he rode under a giant oak tree his head caught in the thick branches and the mule galloped off leaving Absalom hanging in mid-air. When a servant told Joab of Absalom's plight, the general hurried to the oak tree and killed the rebel prince with three spears.

As the signal of victory was sounded, the soldiers stopped fighting on the field of battle. When they came to their general they saw the body of Absalom, and they cast it into a deep pit. Afterward a great heap of stones was raised over the grave of the traitor.

Joab knew that news of the victory must be sent to King David, who sat at the gate in the town of Mahanaim. Ahimaaz wanted to run with the message, but Joab told a Cushite follower who had seen all that had happened to go and tell the king of the battle. Ahimaaz was unhappy to be left behind, so Joab gave him permission to run to the king.

Ahimaaz was a swift runner, and he passed the Cushite; but when he came to the king he had no message. He bowed before King David and said: "All is well."

"Is it well with the young man Absalom?" asked the king anxiously.

"When Joab sent your servant I saw a great tumult, but I did not learn what it was," explained Ahimaaz. He had been a fast runner, but he had no news.

"Turn aside and take your stand here," said the king.

So Ahimaaz turned aside and stood still. At that moment the Cushite entered. The messenger said: "Let my lord the king receive the good news that the Lord has freed you this day from all those that rose up against you."

Then the king asked the messenger: "Is it well with the young man Absalom?"

The Cushite broke the news as gently as he could by saying: "Let the enemies of my lord the king and all who rise up against you for evil be as this young man!"

Then the king was deeply moved and went up to his room and wept. "My son Absalom, my son, my son Absalom! O that I, even I, had died instead of you, Absalom, my son, my son!" cried David.

Soon the monarch returned to his palace at Jerusalem and continued to reign over the tribes of Israel. God blessed him and gave him victory over his enemies.

Prince Absalom rode under a giant oak tree, and his head caught in the thick branches. The mule galloped off leaving him hanging in mid-air.

J. WILKE, ARTIST

—K. Q.

10

SOLOMON BUILDS the TEMPLE

1 KINGS 1:15 to 12:24

WHEN King David was old and
feeble, he chose his son Solomon to be king in his place. Now
Adonijah, another of David's sons, was determined to rule on the
throne. He made a feast and invited all his brothers except Solomon to attend. Nathan the prophet and Zadok the priest heard
of this plot. They hurried to the palace and told Bath-sheba,
David's wife. The king was on his sickbed; but when his wife
told him of the evil plot to usurp the throne, the aged warrior
called Nathan and Zadok to him and commanded them to
anoint Solomon as king of Israel.

The two leaders took Solomon to the town of Gihon. The
priest anointed Solomon, the trumpets were blown, and the people shouted: "Long live King Solomon!" Soon the people of
Jerusalem heard that Solomon had been proclaimed king, and
they followed him, playing upon flutes and singing so loudly
that it seemed they would shake the earth.

The guests at Adonijah's feast heard the tumult and asked:
"Why this noise of the town in uproar?"

While the guests were wondering what had happened, a messenger came in, and Adonijah said: "Enter, for you are a valiant
man and bring good news."

The messenger replied: "No, rather our lord King David has made Solomon king."

Then he went on to explain that the noise was a celebration in honor of the new king, who at that very moment was riding through the streets of Jerusalem on the mule of King David. When the guests heard this, they left hurriedly, and Adonijah quickly repented for his rash deed. He went to the tent of meeting and took hold of the horns of the altar. When Solomon questioned Adonijah, the brother promised complete loyalty to the new king.

Before David died, he called the new king to him and gave him counsel. "I am about to go the way of all the earth," said David to Solomon. "Be strong then and show yourself a man, and keep the charge of the Lord your God, by walking in His ways, by keeping His statutes, His commands, His ordinances, and His decrees, as it is written in the law of Moses, that you may have success in all that you do and in all that you undertake; that the Lord may establish His word that He spoke to me, saying, 'If your sons guard their steps by walking before Me in truth with all their mind and with all their heart, there shall not fail you a man on the throne of Israel.' "

David had dreamed of building a beautiful temple in which the Lord could dwell with His people. But because he had been a man of war and there had been strife during his reign, God told him that the erection of the temple must be left to Solomon. The faithful old king had plans made for the house of God; he also gathered building materials, silver, gold, brass, and precious stones, to make his son's task easier. King David died after ruling Israel for forty years, and he was buried in Jerusalem.

The Queen of Sheba came to visit the king of Israel. She saw his palace and his great wealth. She heard his wise sayings, and she was greatly impressed by his riches and wisdom.

Solomon loved the Lord and followed the good counsel of his father. One night God appeared to him in a dream and said: "Ask what I shall give you."

What would you choose if you could have anything in the world? Would you be as wise in your choice as was this young king?

Solomon asked for wisdom and understanding so that he might judge his people aright and discern between good and evil. The Lord was so pleased with the king's request that He not only gave Solomon wisdom, but He also blessed him with great riches and power. The king wrote three thousand proverbs and composed five thousand songs. He knew many wonderful things about trees, flowers, beasts, birds, and creeping things. Men

The Lord was so pleased with King Solomon's request for wisdom and understanding that He also blessed him with great riches and power.

came to him from other nations to learn of his great wisdom.

The Queen of Sheba came to visit the king of Israel. She saw his palace and his great wealth. She heard his wise sayings, and at last she said to Solomon: "The report which I heard in my own land of your affairs and your wisdom was true; but I would not believe the words until I came and saw with my own eyes, and behold, the half was not told me; you surpass in wisdom and prosperity the report which I heard."

The queen gave Solomon gold, spices, and precious stones. In return Solomon presented many gifts to the Queen of Sheba. The record says that he gave her "all that it pleased her to ask for." Then she returned to her own land with her courtiers and servants.

The time had come to build the temple. Hiram, king of Tyre, a friend of David, supplied Solomon with cedar and other choice woods that were needed for the building. Thousands of men were sent into the mountains of Lebanon to cut down trees. Other thousands cut and squared great stones and polished them for the building. King Hiram also sent Solomon skilled craftsmen who could carve wood and engrave in silver, gold, and brass. Weavers spent months and years making rich and beautiful tapestries. While the house of God was being erected, not a hammer, ax, nor any iron tool was heard in it.

All the stone was prepared at the quarry, and the wood and metal were made ready before they were brought into the temple.

After seven years of constant labor the beautiful house of God was finished. The king set the time for the dedication service, and he invited the people from all over the nation to witness the glorious event. The golden ark and the other furniture that had

The stone was prepared at the quarry, and the wood and metal were made ready before they were brought into the temple. After seven years God's house was finished.

been in the tent of meeting were brought to the temple. Lavish sacrifices were offered, trumpets were blown, and the priests entered the holy place. The cloud of glory of the Lord filled the temple with such splendor that the priests could not perform their service.

Then the king blessed all the people. As he stood before the altar he stretched forth his hands toward heaven, saying: "O Lord, the God of Israel, there is no God like Thee in the heavens above nor upon the earth beneath, who keepest loving faith with Thy servants who walk before Thee with all their heart, who hast kept with Thy servant David, my father, that which thou didst promise him; for Thou didst speak with Thy lips, and with Thy hand Thou hast fulfilled it, as it is this day."

The king also asked for God to bless and guide the nation in times of strife and perplexity, and to forgive and remember no more the people's sins.

For seven days the nation celebrated the dedication of the temple with sacrifices and feasting. On the eighth day Solomon sent the people away to their homes, and everyone rejoiced because of the goodness of the Lord.

Solomon built himself a wonderful palace, and also a beautiful home for one of his wives. He had stables for forty thousand horses. The king had fleets of ships in the Red Sea and in the Mediterranean Sea. The king's navy sailed afar and returned with gold, silver, ivory, apes, and peacocks. The record states that the king made silver in Jerusalem as common as stone and cedars as plentiful as the sycamore trees that grew on the foothills.

In spite of riches and fame, the reign of Solomon did not end in glory. Luxury and wealth was too much for even this wise man. He married many wives from heathen nations, and they turned the king's heart from serving the Lord. Enemies arose against Israel, and there was strife among the twelve tribes. The Lord reproved Solomon, saying: "Inasmuch as this is your attitude and you have not kept My covenant and My statutes, which I have commanded you, I will surely rend the kingdom from you, and will give it to your servant. Nevertheless I will not do it in your days, for David your father's sake; but I will rend it out of the hand of your son. However I will not tear away the whole kingdom; but I will give one tribe to your son, for David my servant's sake and for the sake of Jerusalem which I have chosen."

By this message Solomon knew that the nation would never be strong and united again. The king reigned over Israel forty years, and when he died he was buried in Jerusalem. Rehoboam, the son of Solomon, took the throne of his father.

During Solomon's reign the people had been forced to pay heavy taxes. When Rehoboam became king, the leaders begged him to lighten their burdens. However, the young king refused to listen to the counsel of the old men. He said to the people: "My father made your yoke heavy, but I will add to your yoke; my father chastised you with whips, but I will chastise you with scorpions."

Rebellion broke out among the tribes. When the civil war was ended, Rehoboam had only the tribes of Judah and Benjamin with him. This became the kingdom known as Judah. The other ten tribes chose Jeroboam for their leader, and the second kingdom was known as Israel. From this time on the nation was divided. The ten tribes of Israel continued for about two hundred fifty years before they were overthrown by enemies. The little nation of Judah stood for almost four hundred years, but finally it fell before the attacks of the king of Babylon. Most of the kings of Israel and Judah were wicked men. Only a few of the kings loved God and led the people in the right way. Never again did the nation attain such glory and power as it had during the reign of King Solomon.

PEACOCKS, APES, and GOLD

"IF I get through this class period I'll feel like celebrating." Bette was confiding her worries to her chum, Ruth Gibson, as they entered Miss Mason's room. "You certainly must help me, Ruth, or I'm sunk."

"Don't worry, Bette," said Ruth assuringly. "Roy will take most of the time."

"Yes, I know he is supposed to, but where is he?"

"He'll surely not fail us. He's interested in his report as well as in getting an A grade," replied Ruth encouragingly. When the bell rang signaling the beginning of the class hour, Miss Mason, friendly and efficient as always, introduced the plan of study for the day. "We shall continue the series of reports and discussions we have been having on the life and times of great men of history. Some of our reports have featured Napoleon, Julius Caesar, Socrates, Queen Elizabeth, and Alexander the Great. Today we are going back about twenty-five hundred years to the time of King Solomon. Roy and Bette Barrett and Ruth Gibson have this report. Will the three of you come and take seats at the table in front of the class?"

"This is torture," whispered Bette to her friend as they walked forward. "And where, oh, where, is Roy?"

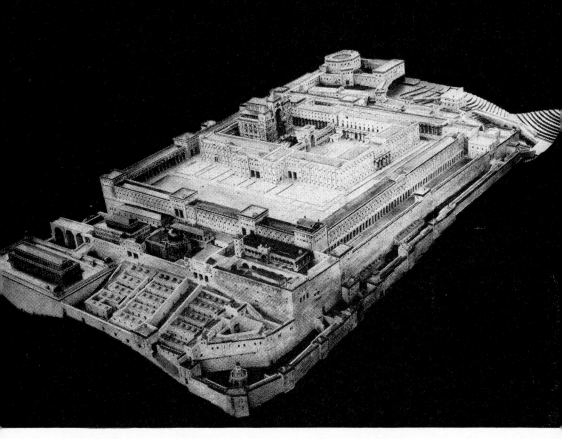

This model of Solomon's Temple depicts some of its glory. The temple was about one hundred feet long and thirty-three feet wide, and it had two main rooms.

The two girls were seated, ready to begin their reports, when the door opened, and Roy hurried into the room. "I'm sorry to be late," he explained to Miss Mason, who gave him a reproving look. "But I was tracking down some material I learned about the last minute. You'll see what I mean, Miss Mason, when I give my report."

"Very well, Roy," replied the teacher. By her look, however, she did not seem to be convinced that Roy's tardiness was necessary. "Let's start at once," she added.

Bette, the leader in the discussion, introduced the subject of the first speaker. "We chose the life and times of King Solo-

mon because he always seemed interesting and romantic," the girl began. "He was the son of King David, and when he took the throne of his father the nation was in its golden age. Ruth will tell us about the wonderful Temple Solomon built."

Ruth arose and went to the blackboard where she had drawn a diagram. "Solomon's Temple was built in Jerusalem," she explained. "It was to take the place of the tent of meeting the children of Israel had constructed in the wilderness."

"I found that this Temple was about one hundred feet long and thirty-three feet wide," Ruth continued, pointing to her drawing on the blackboard. "The ceiling was some fifty feet high. Huge stones were used in the walls, and cedar beams from the forests of Mount Lebanon made the roof.

"The Temple had two chief rooms like the tent of meeting. There was the holy place and the holy of holies. In the front of the Temple was a porch or court where the people could gather.

"It's interesting to find that all the lumber and stone was cut and prepared before it was brought to the Temple area in Jerusalem. There wasn't any noisy hammering or sawing in the Temple while it was being built.

"Solomon's Temple was ornamented with much gold. It stood in its glory until Nebuchadnezzar, king of Babylon, captured Jerusalem and burned the Temple and the city in 588 b.c."

After this report, Bette introduced her twin brother by saying: "Roy will tell us about Solomon's empire and how he became rich."

"We always hear about Solomon's wives," began Roy; but we don't always realize that he was a military leader and a busi-

King Solomon was a mighty king and he had a large army with war chariots and horsemen to protect the nation.

SIR E. J. POYNTER, ARTIST

RISCHGITZ STUDIOS

The Queen of Sheba heard that Solomon was very wise, and one time she made a trip
to Jerusalem to meet him. She found the king had an ivory throne overlaid with gold.

nessman. In the Bible we read that Solomon had a navy in the
Red Sea that sailed to distant parts of Africa for treasures. King
Hiram sent his sailors with Solomon's sailors, and they brought
back much gold from Ophir. The king had another fleet in
the Mediterranean Sea that sailed to far-off lands and returned
with silver, gold, ivory, apes, and peacocks. That must have
been quite a cargo to carry on those sailing vessels. In fact, the
king had so many treasures that it was said silver was as common as cobblestones in Jerusalem, and cedar was as cheap as
sycamore wood.

"I found that Solomon had copper mines in Edom, the country south of Palestine. Archaeologists, the men who dig for

ancient cities and monuments, have found the place where one of Solomon's smelters was built. The king must have had many copper mines, for in the seventh chapter of First Kings we read about all the copper vessels he had made for the Temple. King Hiram's metal workers cast these vessels on the plain of Jordan not far from Succoth. They probably did the work there because there was good clay to make the molds.

"Solomon had a good-sized army, too. He had war chariots and horsemen. One of the large stables, with stone hitching posts, stalls, and mangers from which the horses ate grain, has been unearthed at Megiddo. More than a thousand horses could be stabled there at one time. The king must have been quite interested in horses. He had hundreds of them brought from Egypt and other countries. He built special cities for his chariots and his horsemen. In fact, Solomon was quite a horse trader. He bought horses and chariots from Egypt, and he sold them to the kings of Syria and to the other countries in the north. I will read two verses from the Bible which tell about his trade in horses: 'Solomon's transport of horses was between Egypt and Kuë; the king's traders received them from Kuë at a price, and a chariot could be imported from Egypt for six hundred shekels of silver and a horse for a hundred and fifty. In this manner they carried on trade with all the kings of the Hittites and the kings of the Arameans.'

"Solomon was a wise man in business, and people from all parts of the world brought gifts to him and asked his counsel."

Roy picked up a large envelope from the table and drew out some photographs. "This morning I found that one of my friends had some pictures of the ancient stables at Megiddo for

me. I have them here and will pass them around for all of you to see," said Roy.

"That must be why he was late," Bette whispered to Ruth.

"I'm sure Captain Lane got them for him."

"Here is a picture of what Solomon's Temple may have looked like," Roy explained, holding a large picture up before the class. "I also have a picture of the copper smelter used in Solomon's time, that each of you can see. It was discovered a few years ago in Arabia."

When Roy had completed his report and gathered up his photographs, Miss Mason said: "Those interesting pictures must have been the reason you were late."

"Yes, that's right, Miss Mason," replied the youth. "Captain Lane called me a half hour before class and said that the postman had just brought them to him. The captain wrote to a friend to get them for our report. They came in the nick of time."

"We appreciate them, Roy, and also thank Captain Lane for his help," the teacher declared appreciatively. "Now, Bette," she continued, "we'll hear your story."

"The wise decisions of Solomon interested me so much I want to tell you about it," said the girl as she stood beside the speaker's table. "The Queen of Sheba heard that Solomon was very wise, and one time she made the trip to Jerusalem to see him. She brought gold, spices, and precious gems to Solomon. She found the king seated on an ivory throne overlaid with gold. The queen saw the beautiful palace and the many servants, and finally she said she had not heard even half of the truth about Solomon's greatness and wisdom.

he king listened to the charges of the two women, nd then he commanded: "Bring me a sword."

SCHOPIN, ARTIST; GRAMSTORFF

—K. Q.

"The Bible gives us one of the king's wise decisions. It was like this: Two women came to King Solomon one day and asked for his judgment. One woman said: 'I live in the same house with this other woman. One night her child smothered to death in its bed and she arose in the night and took my son from me while I was asleep and put her dead child where my boy was. In the morning I found her dead child in my bed.'

"The other woman denied the charge and said it was her child who was alive and well. The king listened and finally said: 'Bring me a sword.' When the sword was brought, he commanded: 'Divide the living child in two, and give half to one and half to the other.' When the real mother of the child heard this, she cried out for the king to give the living child to the other woman. The false woman said: 'Divide it.' Then the king gave the child to its mother, for he saw which woman had true love for the baby.

"I think that was a shrewd test," Bette concluded. "I'm sure most lawyers would not be clever enough to solve a case in that way."

Br-r-rg! The bell in the hall clanged the end of the class period.

"Your report on Solomon has been excellent," Miss Mason announced. "Class dismissed."

After the students had hurried from the classroom, Bette turned to her brother and gave a sigh of relief. "Whew! I'm glad that's over. You had me scared at the beginning of the class, Roy. I thought you'd never get here."

"If you had seen me tearing down Maple Street on my bicycle you'd have known I felt the same way." Roy gathered up his pictures and papers. "Come on, Ruth and Bette, it's time for lunch. Let's go to the cafeteria. I'll buy dessert for all of us to celebrate."

"It's a deal!" exclaimed two laughing girls as they hurried down the school corridor. Ruth added: "I am sure Solomon would have given several pieces of gold for a dish of ice cream, if he had only tasted it once."

11

ΣLIJAH, FIGHTER *for* GOD

1 KINGS 17:1 to 2 KINGS 2:15

DURING the reign of Ahab, seventh king of Israel, a brave fighter for God's truth suddenly appeared in the royal court. This stranger was Elijah, the prophet, and he came from his home in the mountains of Gilead, east of the river Jordan, to stand before Ahab, the weak and wicked king. The monarch was dominated by his heathen wife, Jezebel, an ambitious woman who wanted to make all Israel worship the pagan idol Baal.

When Elijah saw his people sinking deeper and deeper into idolatry, he determined to reprove the king for his evil deeds. The man of God stood before Ahab and said: "As the Lord, the God of Israel, lives, before whom I stand, there shall be neither dew nor rain these years, except by my word." Then, without waiting for an answer, the prophet left the court.

The king was stunned by this strange message, and he determined to kill this prophet. But the Lord was with Elijah and gave him this instruction: "Depart from here and turn eastward, and hide yourself by the Brook Cherith, that is east of the Jordan, and you shall drink from the brook; and I have commanded the ravens to feed you there." Although Ahab searched for the prophet, he could not find him.

(115)

After Elijah had commanded that twelve jars of water be poured over the sacrifice, he prayed earnestly for God to send fire from heaven.

N. BRICE, ARTIST; © P. P. P. A.

The prophet lived in hiding beside the Brook Cherith. Every morning and evening the ravens flew to him bringing bread and meat. As long as there was water in the brook, Elijah could stay in this safe retreat. But a day came when the severe drought dried up the trickling stream. Then Elijah was told to go to Zarephath, a town in Zidon, outside of the kingdom of Israel. As the prophet came to the city gate, he saw a widow gathering sticks to make a fire. "Bring me, I pray you, a little water in a vessel that I may drink," he called to the woman.

As she went to get a jar of water, he called to her again and said: "Bring me, I pray you, a morsel of food in your hand."

"As the Lord your God lives," she replied, "I have nothing but a handful of meal in the jar and a little oil in a cruse; and

The prophet Elijah lived in hiding beside the brook. Every morning and evening the ravens flew to him bringing bread and meat. He drank water from the trickling stream.

W. WILKE, ARTIST

now I am gathering a few sticks that I may go in and prepare it for myself and my son, that we may eat it and die."

"Fear not," said the prophet; "go and do as you have said; but first make me from it a little cake, and bring it to me, and afterward make one for yourself and for your son. For thus says the Lord, the God of Israel: 'The jar of meal shall not be exhausted nor the cruse of oil spent until the day that the Lord sends rain upon the ground.'"

The woman had faith in Elijah's words, and day after day her family had food to eat. There was always meal in the jar, and there was enough oil to mix with it to make cakes for her family.

One day her young son became sick and died. The mother came to Elijah in her grief, and the prophet said: "Give me your son."

He carried the dead child upstairs to his room and laid him upon his own bed. Then he stretched himself over the body three times and called upon God: "I pray Thee, may this child's life return to him again." Elijah's prayer was answered, for the child arose at once, and the man of God took him downstairs to his happy mother.

In the third year of the drought and famine, Elijah received instruction from heaven to tell King Ahab that the Lord would bring rain to the parched earth.

When the wicked king saw Elijah, he shouted angrily: "Is it you, you troubler of Israel?"

"I have not troubled Israel," said the brave prophet, "but you and your father's house, in that you have forsaken the commands of the Lord and have gone after the Baal. Now therefore send and gather to me all Israel, to Mount Carmel, together with the four hundred and fifty prophets of the Baal and the four hundred prophets of the Asherah, who eat at Jezebel's table."

The king sent messengers throughout the land calling the people and the false prophets to assemble on Mount Carmel. When they arrived, Elijah stood before them and said: "How long are you going to limp upon two diverse opinions? If the Lord be God, follow Him, but if the Baal, follow him."

The people were silent; they knew they had disobeyed the God of heaven. Then Elijah said: "I, even I only, am left as a prophet of the Lord, but the prophets of the Baal are four hundred and fifty men. Let them therefore give us two bulls, and let them choose one bull for themselves and cut it in pieces and lay it on the wood but make no fire, and I will prepare the other bull and place it on the wood, but I will make no fire. Then call you on the name of your god and I will call on the name of the Lord; and the god who answers by fire, he is God."

Thereupon all the people answered and said: "It is a fair test!"

It was decided that the priests of Baal should be the first to build an altar and put their sacrifice upon it. From early morning until noon they called on their god Baal, but nothing happened. Elijah watched the heathen priests, and he mocked them, saying: "Cry with a loud voice, for he is a god; either he is meditating, or he has gone aside, or he is on a journey, or perhaps he is asleep and needs to be awakened!"

Baal's priests became excited. They shouted louder, and they slashed themselves with swords until blood gushed out upon them; but there was no answer from their idol.

Elijah sat down, tired and worn, and bowed his head in prayer. His servant went to scan the horizon for signs of coming rain

Soon the sky was dark, and there was a downpour of rain. Since Ahab could not find his way through the storm, Elijah ran before his chariot until they came to Jezreel.

In the afternoon Elijah was ready to make his test. After calling all the people to him, he rebuilt the altar of the Lord that had been broken down and long-forgotten. He also made a ditch around the altar. After placing the sacrifice on the wood, the prophet had twelve jars of water poured over the sacrifice, and the water ran down and filled the trench around the altar. Then Elijah prayed earnestly to the Lord of heaven.

Suddenly fire flashed from heaven and burned the sacrifice and the wood. It consumed the stones and licked up the water in the trench. The God of heaven had answered Elijah's prayer. When the people saw this tremendous power from heaven, they fell on their faces and said: "The Lord, He is God; the Lord, He is God."

The priests of Baal, seeing that they were defeated, started to run away; but Elijah shouted for the people to catch the false prophets. These evil men were slain because they had deceived the nation and led the people to do wickedly.

King Ahab had witnessed the power of God, and his heart must have been thrilled by the wonderful demonstration. Elijah said to the monarch: "Go up, eat and drink; for there is the rushing sound of rain."

While the king was eating and drinking, the prophet took his servant, and together they climbed to the mountain. Elijah sat down, tired and worn from the day of test. While his servant went to scan the horizon over the blue Mediterranean Sea, the prophet humbly bowed his head and prayed for his people. Again and again Elijah sent the man to look out over the water, but it was not until the seventh time that he came running to Elijah and said: "There is a cloud the size of a man's hand, rising out of the sea."

Immediately the prophet commanded: "Go up, say to Ahab, 'Harness your steeds and go down, so that the rain may not stop you.'"

Soon the sky was dark with clouds, a mighty wind struck the mountainside, and with it came a downpour of rain! Since the king could not find his way through the storm, Elijah girded up his garments and ran before Ahab's chariot until they came to the entrance of Jezreel, the capital city.

When King Ahab reached the palace and told Queen Jezebel how Elijah had killed her priests of Baal, she sent a messenger to the prophet who lay sleeping at the city gate. The queen threatened Elijah, saying: "As surely as you are Elijah and I am Jezebel, so may God requite me and worse, if I do not make your life as the life of one of them by tomorrow about this time."

Fear overcame the man of God who had been so courageous on Mount Carmel. He arose quickly and started down the road on the run toward the town of Beersheba. Tired, hungry, and exhausted, the prophet finally stopped to rest. He was so discouraged he wanted to die.

After he had been refreshed by sleep, an angel of the Lord gave Elijah food. Then he arose and traveled for forty days. At last he came to Mount Horeb, far to the south, where Moses had once lived. The discouraged prophet found a cave in the mountainside and crawled into it.

"What are you doing here, Elijah?" asked the Lord.

The prophet tried to explain that he was the only one left in Israel who loved God. He said he was afraid the king would kill him.

The Lord told the prophet to return to his task in Israel. He informed Elijah that there were actually seven thousand loyal followers of the Lord in the nation, who had not bowed to the Baal.

On his way back to the capital city, Elijah met a young farmer, Elisha, plowing in the field. The prophet threw his cloak over the farm boy—a sign that he was called to God's service. Elisha accepted the challenge and went with the prophet. For several years Elisha served his master. The two men visited the schools of the prophets, where young men were trained to love and serve God.

One day while Elisha was traveling with Elijah from Gilgal to Bethel, the young man was made to realize that his master

A chariot of blazing glory took Elijah up to heaven, and Elisha saw his master no more.

W. WILKE, ARTIST

was soon to leave him. When they stopped at Bethel, Elijah said: "Elisha, remain here, I pray you, for the Lord has sent me to Jericho."

"As the Lord lives and as you yourself are alive, I will not leave you," the young man replied.

So the two went on to Jericho, where young men from the school of the prophets met them. They said to Elisha: "Do you know that the Lord is about to take away your master from being your leader today?"

"Yes, I know it. Hold your peace," he said.

Elijah said that he was going on to the Jordan River, and he told Elisha that he could remain at Jericho. But the young man refused to part from his master, and the two went on together to the Jordan River. Fifty of the young men from the school followed at a distance to see what might happen. They saw Elijah strike the water of the river with his cloak and the waters divide, so that the two men could walk across on dry ground.

As soon as they had passed over, Elijah said to Elisha: "Ask what I shall do for you, before I am taken from you."

"Let there be now a twofold share of your spirit upon me!" pleaded Elisha.

"You have asked a hard thing," Elijah answered, "still, if you see me as I am being taken from you, so shall it be with you; but if not, it shall not be so."

As they were talking a chariot of fire and glory, drawn by horses of fire, suddenly came between the two men, and Elijah was caught up to heaven by a whirlwind.

As Elisha looked, he cried out: "My father, my father! the

chariots of Israel and its horsemen!" Elisha saw his beloved master no more, and in sorrow he tore his garments. Then as he looked down he saw Elijah's cloak lying on the ground. The young man picked it up and hurried back to the Jordan River. When Elisha struck the waters, behold, they parted as they had for the mighty prophet. Thus Elisha knew that he was to take the place of Elijah and that God had given him power to do a great work for the nation.

ELISHA, PERFORMER of WONDERS

2 KINGS 2:19 to 4:44

W HEN the sons of the prophets saw that the Lord was with Elisha, they said: "The spirit of Elijah is upon Elisha."

Truly this man was a doer of good deeds. He was always helping people. Before he left Jericho, the men of the city asked his advice as to how the spring of water which supplied the people could be made fit to drink. Elisha took salt water and poured it into the spring, and the waters became pure and sweet.

Elisha journeyed northward on the road to Bethel. While he was passing a town, some boys came out and jeered at him. "Go up, you baldhead; go up, baldhead," they shouted.

The prophet pronounced a curse upon the children for their wicked language, and suddenly two bears came out of the woods and mangled forty-two of the youth. God allowed this fearful punishment to come to teach boys and girls not to make fun of other people. By dishonoring the prophet Elisha, these children were sinning against God.

One day a widow of one of the sons of the prophets came to Elisha. "My husband your servant, is dead," she said, "and you know that your servant feared the Lord; but the creditor has come to take my two children to be his slaves."

"What shall I do for you?" Elisha asked. "Tell me; what have you in the house?"

"Your maidservant has nothing in the house, except a flask of oil," she answered.

"Go," said he, "borrow vessels abroad of all your neighbors, even empty vessels not a few. Then go in and shut the door upon yourself and your sons, and pour out into all these vessels, and when one is full set it aside."

The woman followed Elisha's instructions and shut the door upon herself and her sons. She began to pour oil into the vessels while her sons kept bringing pots and pans to her. As soon as she had one filled she said: "Bring me another." Finally, when there was not another pot or pan in her house, the oil stopped.

Then the widow hurried back to Elisha and told him what had happened.

"Go," said he, "sell the oil and pay your debts, and you and your sons can live on what is left."

Some time later the great and good prophet went to Shunem, a village in the hills north of Mount Carmel. As Elisha walked down the street, a prominent woman saw him and invited him to her home for dinner. She was so interested in the man of God that she said to her husband: "See here, I am sure that this is a holy man of God who is continually passing by us. Let us make now a little enclosed roof chamber, and let us put a bed for him there, a table, a chair, and a lamp, so that whenever he comes to us, he can go in there." Elisha appreciated the family's kindness in giving him this guest room.

When the student showed Elisha the spot where the ax had fallen into the water, the prophet cut off a stick and threw it in the stream, and the iron axhead floated on top.

He noticed that the man and his wife had no children. So the prophet revealed to the woman God's message that He would bless her home with a son. It was a happy day in that family when a baby boy was born. Several years passed, and the lad grew strong. One day he went out into the harvest field where the reapers were cutting grain. The sun's rays were hot, and the boy's head hurt. He cried: "My head, my head!"

The father realized that his son had a sunstroke. He called a servant and said: "Carry him to his mother." When he had been carried to his mother, the lad sat on her lap until noon and then he died.

The sorrowing mother hurried to Mount Carmel to find Elisha. She told the prophet what had happened to her only son. The man of God sent his servant, Gehazi, to restore the child to life. The servant placed Elisha's staff on the dead boy's face, as his master commanded; but there was no sound or response from the child.

When Elisha came to the house with the mother, he went to the room where the dead child lay. Closing the door, he prayed earnestly to the Lord. Then he leaned over and placed his face against the child's face; he put his hands upon the boy's hands. The child's flesh grew warm, but he did not move. Elisha paced back and forth, and prayed again. Suddenly the boy sneezed seven times and opened his eyes.

Elisha's servant brought the mother to the room, and when she saw her son alive and well she rejoiced. "Take up your son," said Elisha. The mother thanked God and bowed before the prophet in gratitude for his kindness to her family.

There was a famine in the land when Elisha went to visit the school of the prophets at Gilgal. Food was scarce, and it was the custom for students to go out into the fields to find vegetables for stew. One of the men gathered some wild gourds and cut them up into the pot in which they were cooking the food. When the men sat down to eat, they noticed the peculiar taste of the food and cried out: "O man of God, there is death in the pot."

Elisha said, "Bring meal," and when they brought meal, he threw it into the pot and told the people that there was now no danger of poisoning. They ate the stew, and no harm came to any of them.

One day a man brought Elisha twenty loaves of barley bread and some fresh vegetables. The prophet thought at once of his hungry students, and he said: "Give them to the people that they may eat; for thus says the Lord: 'They shall eat and have some left.'"

Although it seemed that twenty small loaves of bread would not go far among more than a hundred men, yet God blessed the food, and all of the people had plenty to eat, and there was some left over. Again and again the prophet's faith was rewarded. He believed that God would care for His people if they would trust in Him.

In one of the schools of the prophets there was not enough room for all the students. They decided to go to the bank of the Jordan River and cut down trees to use in building another house. Elisha went with the men, and while they were cutting down the trees, the iron ax that one of the students was using fell into the water.

"Alas, my master! for it was borrowed," called the student.

"Where did it fall?" asked the man of God.

When the student showed Elisha the spot where the ax had fallen into the water, the prophet cut off a stick and threw it in the water and the iron axhead floated on the surface.

"Take it up," said Elisha. The young man reached out his hand and took the ax that had been rescued by the prophet.

Thus in the little things of everyday life, Elisha called upon God for help, and the prophet was never disappointed. How often in our daily tasks we may ask God to help us! He is ready to assist us in every time of need, for there is nothing too small for Him.

Life and customs of Bible lands continue much the same today as two thousand years ago. (Left) A weaver sits at his loom under a papyrus shelter.

(Above) A Bedouin waters his camels at an oasis. (Right center) Plowing on the plain of Sharon with a camel supplying the needed power. (Right) Winnowing grain on a threshing floor to separate the wheat from the chaff at harvesttime.

13

A BRAVE GIRL SAVES a LEPER

2 KINGS 5:1 to 5:27

SYRIA, the country directly north of Israel, had made war against Israel since the days of King Ahab. During the time of Elisha, the prophet, the Syrians raided the country and carried away some of the people who lived near the city of Samaria. Among the prisoners taken to the city of Damascus was a girl who had seen the prophet and heard of his wonderful deeds.

This girl became a serving maid to the wife of Naaman, commander of the Syrian army. Naaman was a great man, highly esteemed by the king; but he was not happy, for he was a leper. In those days there was no cure for leprosy. The skin of a leper turns white and rots away; eventually death comes to the victim.

The captive maid loved Naaman's wife, and she was sad because her master had this incurable disease. One day she said to her mistress: "Would that my master were with the prophet who is in Samaria! Then he would cure him of his leprosy."

When Naaman heard these words, hope flamed in his heart. He decided to ask the king of Syria for permission to go to Israel in search of a cure.

(133)

The captive maid said one day to her mistress:
"Would that my master were with the prophet in
Samaria! Then he would cure him of his leprosy."

W. WILKE, ARTIST

"Go now," said the king, "and I will send along a letter to the king of Israel." Naaman set out with chariots, horsemen, and soldiers, and he also carried ten talents of silver, six thousand shekels of gold, and ten beautiful robes as gifts for anyone who could rid him of his fearful disease.

Naaman thought that the king of Israel would surely be the one who could help him. He arrived in Samaria and presented the letter from the Syrian king to the ruler of Israel. The letter read as follows: "Now when this letter reaches you, be informed that I have sent to you my servant Naaman, that you may cure him of his leprosy."

After the monarch had read the letter, he threw it on the floor, tore his robes, and shouted: "Am I a god to kill and to make alive, that this man is sending to me to cure a man of his leprosy? Take note and observe how he is seeking occasion against me."

Discouraged by the strange actions of the king, Naaman felt like returning at once to his home in Syria. When Elisha heard how the king of Israel had given this Syrian commander no hope of healing, he sent a message to the king saying: "Why have you torn your garments? I pray you, let him come to me, that he may know that there is a prophet in Israel."

So Naaman and his men rode in their chariots to the house of Elisha. The prophet did not come out to see this officer from a foreign land. Instead, he sent Gehazi, his servant, who said: "Go and wash in the Jordan seven times, and your flesh shall be restored and you shall be clean."

The Syrian became very angry, for he felt that he had been insulted. He said: "Here I have been saying to myself, 'He will

When he came to the Jordan River, Naaman got down from his chariot, took off his robe, and plunged into the water. He dipped seven times as Elisha had commanded.

surely come out and stand and call on the name of the Lord his God, and wave his hand toward the place and cure the leper.' Are not Amana and Pharpar, the rivers of Damascus, better than all the waters of Israel? Could I not wash in them and be clean?"

Naaman drove away from Elisha's house in a rage. When he was calm enough to listen, one of his wise servants said to him: "My father, if the prophet had demanded of you some great thing, would you not have done it? How much rather then, when he has said to you, 'Wash and be clean'?"

The Syrian paused to think about these words. He was going to die of leprosy unless he could be healed. Why should he not follow the prophet's simple instructions?

Driving eastward until he came to the Jordan River, Naaman got down from his chariot, took off his robe, and plunged into the water. He dipped himself seven times, as Elisha had commanded. There were ugly white patches of skin and raw sores on his body; but when he arose from the water the seventh time, Naaman's skin was like the skin of a child. He was cured of his leprosy!

Quickly the chariots drove back to Elisha's house. Naaman hurried into the house and stood before the prophet. "Verily, now I know that there is no God in all the earth, but in Israel," said Naaman. "Now therefore, I pray you, accept a present from your servant."

"As the Lord lives whom I serve I will take nothing," said Elisha.

Although Naaman urged Elisha to accept rich presents, the prophet would take nothing. Now, Gehazi, Elisha's servant, listened to all that was said, and he longed to have some of the silver and gold. He coveted the beautiful robes, for his own clothing was shabby and patched. Therefore, after Naaman had started northward toward his home, Gehazi hurried after him. When the Syrian officer saw the man running along the road, he stopped his chariots and went back to meet Elisha's servant. "Is it well?" he asked.

"All is well," said Gehazi. "My master sent me saying, 'There have just now come to me two young men of the prophetic order from the highlands of Ephraim. I pray you, give them a talent of silver and two festal garments.'"

Of course, Gehazi was lying; but Naaman was so happy to be healed of his leprosy that he gave the servant more than he had requested. "Consent to accept two talents," said Naaman, heaping the treasures upon the man.

Gehazi returned to his house and hid the gifts. Then he went and stood before Elisha. The prophet said: "Where have you been, Gehazi?"

"Your servant has not been away anywhere," lied Gehazi.

"Was I not present in spirit when the man turned from his chariot to meet you?" said the prophet. "Is it a time to accept money, and garments, and olive orchards and vineyards, and sheep and oxen, and menservants and maidservants? The leprosy of Naaman shall fasten upon you and upon your descendants forever."

So Gehazi left Elisha's presence a leper as white as snow.

It must have been a wonderful day when Naaman arrived home. His wife surely rejoiced when she saw that her husband was free from the fearful disease. How happy the captive maid must have been for her master! Not only had he returned well and strong, but now he worshiped the true God whom she loved. Because this faithful girl had been true to her God in a foreign land, her prayers had been answered, and she had helped to save a leper from an untimely death!

14

ELISHA CAPTURES an ARMY

2 KINGS 6:8 to 13:20

ONCE when the king of Syria was at war with Israel, he counseled with his officers as to how to move secretly so as to capture the Israelites by strategy. Time after time the Syrian army would attempt to surround Israel's forces, only to find that they had escaped. The king thought that there was surely a traitor in his army who was giving military secrets to the enemy. Therefore he called his officers together and asked: "Will you not tell me, who of us is for the king of Israel?"

"There is no one, my lord, O king!" said one of his servants, "but Elisha, the prophet who is in Israel, tells the king of Israel the words that you speak in your bedroom."

"Go and see where he is," said the king, "that I may send and take him."

"Behold he is in Dothan," a servant reported.

Immediately the king of Syria sent a large force of warriors with horses and chariots to surround that city. They came swiftly in the night, and the next morning when Elisha and his servant awoke they saw the enemy army surrounding the city.

"Alas, my master! What shall we do?" cried Elisha's servant.

"Fear not," said the prophet, "for they who are with us are

(139)

The astonished servant saw the mountains about the city full of horses and chariots of fire to give protection from the enemy.

WILKE, ARTIST

more than they who are with them." Then Elisha prayed and said: "O Lord, open now his eyes that he may see."

The astonished servant then saw the mountains around about the city full of horses and chariots of fire. The Lord had sent His angels to protect His servants in time of great danger.

Soon the Syrian army advanced to capture Elisha. When they came near, the prophet prayed: "Smite now this people with blindness."

The helpless soldiers became blind and hopelessly lost. They wandered about the town, not knowing where they were. Elisha came to them and said: "This is neither the way nor the city. Follow me and I will bring you to the man whom you seek!"

Through the power of the Lord, Elisha was able to capture the enemy army and lead it to Samaria to the king of Israel. The prophet then asked God to open the eyes of the captured men. When the king of Israel saw the enemy helpless before him, he asked eagerly of the prophet: "My father, shall I slay them?"

"You shall not slay," replied Elisha; "would you slay those whom you have not taken prisoner with your sword and with your bow? Set bread and water before them, that they may eat and drink and go to their master."

Then the king made a great feast for the Syrian army, and when they had eaten, Elisha sent the warriors home. They gave a full report to the king of Syria as to how well they had been treated. As a result of this kindness on the part of Israel, the two nations became friendly once more, and the Syrians did not attack God's people for many years.

Elisha continued faithful in his work for the Lord. He showed the people the way of right and helped them in times of

When the window was opened, Elisha commanded: "Shoot." Joash let the arrow fly. "The Lord's arrow of victory and the arrow of victory over Syria," cried the prophet.

crisis. When the prophet was old, he became seriously ill. Joash, the king of Israel, came to visit the prophet. He was troubled because once more the Syrians were striking hard against Israel. With tears in his eyes he said to Elisha: "My father, my father! the chariots of Israel and its horsemen!" These were the same words Elisha had spoken when the prophet Elijah had been taken to heaven.

The king meant to inform Elisha that he was helpless before the strong enemy from the north. He longed to know what he should do and what the prophet's counsel was in this crisis.

"Take bow and arrows," Elisha said.

Then Elisha took up a bow and arrows, and he said to the king of Israel: "Lay your hand upon the bow."

When the king had done so, Elisha put his hand upon the king's hand.

Then the prophet said: "Open the window toward the east."

When the window was opened, Elisha commanded: "Shoot."

Joash drew back the bow and let the arrow fly swiftly. "The Lord's arrow of victory and the arrow of victory over Syria," exclaimed Elisha, "for you are to fight Syria in Aphek to a finish."

"Take the arrows," said the prophet.

When the king had taken them, Elisha commanded once more: "Strike on the ground."

The king struck the ground three times and then stopped. Elisha was disappointed because the man had not continued striking the ground. "You should have struck five or six times," said Elisha, "then you would have fought Syria to a finish. But now you will defeat Syria only three times."

Soon after this incident the aged prophet died. The nation lost a kind and faithful friend who had for many years been a mighty leader in Israel for God.

Memory Verses

"David spake unto the Lord the words of this song in the day that the Lord had delivered him out of the hand of all his enemies, and out of the hand of Saul: and he said, The Lord is my rock, and my fortress, and my deliverer; the God of my rock; in Him will I trust: He is my shield, and the horn of my salvation, my high tower, and my refuge, my Saviour; Thou savest me from violence." 2 Samuel 22:1-3.

"Solomon said, Thou hast showed unto Thy servant David my father great mercy, according as he walked before Thee in truth, and in righteousness, and in uprightness of heart with Thee; and Thou hast kept for him this great kindness, that Thou hast given him a son to sit on his throne, as it is this day. And now, O Lord my God, Thou hast made Thy servant king instead of David my father: and I am but a little child: I know not how to go out or come in. . . . Give therefore Thy servant an understanding heart to judge Thy people, that I may discern between good and bad: for who is able to judge this Thy so great a people?" 1 Kings 3:6-9.

"He answered, Fear not: for they that be with us are more than they that be with them." 2 Kings 6:16.

15

JONAH'S NARROW ESCAPE

THE BOOK OF JONAH

FAR to the east of Israel and Syria arose the great empire of Assyria. Its kings were mighty, and when they sent out their armies they conquered the smaller nations. When the king of Israel heard of the Assyrians, he was afraid, and rightly so, for the day was soon to come when the fierce warriors from Nineveh would capture Samaria and carry the ten tribes of Israel into exile.

In the little country of Judah, the land of the two tribes of Benjamin and Judah, there lived a prophet named Jonah. The Lord sent a message to him saying: "Arise, go to Nineveh, that great city, and preach against it; for their wickedness has come up before Me."

Perhaps the prophet was afraid to go to the capital city of Assyria, for he may have dreaded to face strange people in a foreign land. Anyway, Jonah hurried westward to Joppa instead of starting eastward for Nineveh. When the frightened man arrived at the seaport, he bought a ticket on a ship sailing for Tarshish, a city far to the west. Now, thought Jonah, I will get away where God cannot find me. Now I can avoid going to Nineveh!

After the ship had sailed from the harbor, the prophet went

down into the hold and fell asleep. Soon a terrific storm struck the boat. The wind howled, and the waves crashed over the sides of the vessel. Even the sailors were frightened, and each man called on his pagan gods for help. The storm grew so severe that it seemed that the ship would be swamped. In desperation the crew threw the cargo overboard to lighten the ship.

The captain went down into the hold of the ship and found Jonah sound asleep. "Why are you sleeping?" asked the captain. "Get up; call upon your god. Perhaps that god will bethink himself of us, that we perish not."

The storm increased in fury, and the sailors gave up hope of reaching land. Then they said one to another: "Come, let us cast lots, that we may know upon whose account this disaster has befallen us."

So they cast lots, and the lot fell upon Jonah. They looked at this man who had obtained passage on the ship, and they said: "Tell us, now, for what reason this disaster has befallen us. What is your business? Whence do you come? What is your country? And from what people are you?"

Jonah told the men that he was a Hebrew and that he had run away from his God-given duty. He told them that he worshiped the Creator of the heavens and the earth. When the men heard this, they were terrified and said: "What a wicked thing you have done!"

After talking together, the sailors asked Jonah: "What shall we do with you, that the sea may become calm for us?"

"Pick me up," said Jonah, "and cast me into the sea, so that the sea may be calm for you; for I know that this great storm is upon you because of me."

The sailors refused to throw Jonah overboard, and they rowed the boat harder in an attempt to reach land. But the heavy waves beat against the ship and the storm grew worse and worse. Finally they cried unto the Lord in their terror and said: "O Lord, we beseech Thee, let us not perish for this man's life; and lay not up against us innocent blood; for Thou, O Lord, dost do as Thou pleasest."

So they took up Jonah and tossed him overboard into the roaring sea! When they had done this, the storm abated and the waves grew calm.

Jonah was tossed about in the water, and suddenly he saw "a great fish" swimming toward him. He cried out in fear and terror. Then he saw the huge mouth of the fish open. The next thing Jonah knew, he felt himself being sucked into the giant jaws and swallowed! Down, down, down he went into the belly of the fish. "The Lord had assigned a great fish to swallow up Jonah," says the Bible.

For three days and three nights Jonah tossed about in the stomach of the great fish. He must have been frightened and sick at heart. He knew what was happening, however, and he prayed to God, promising that if he was saved alive he would obey and go to Nineveh to preach.

After three days the fish threw Jonah up on dry land, and the prophet returned to his home, thankful that his life had been spared. Soon the message of the Lord came to Jonah a second time, saying: "Arise, go to Nineveh, that great city, and proclaim unto it the proclamation which I am about to tell you."

This time Jonah did not hesitate. He started at once for Nineveh, and when he reached the great city on the banks of

Jonah was tossed into the water, and suddenly he saw "a great fish." He cried in terror when it opened its mouth.

W. WILKE, ARTIST

Jonah started for Nineveh, and when he reached the city on the banks of the Tigris he went through the city shouting: "Forty days more, and Nineveh shall be overthrown."

the Tigris River he went through the streets shouting: "Forty days more, and Nineveh shall be overthrown."

The people of Nineveh were wicked, but when they heard this warning they began to mourn. The king sent out a decree that every person should fast and repent of his sins and call upon God. When the Lord saw that the Assyrians wanted to do right, He determined not to destroy Nineveh. But when Jonah found that the city was to be spared, he was angry. It seemed that his work had been in vain. He decided that life wasn't worth living, and he prayed: "Now, therefore, O Lord, take my life, I pray Thee, from me. For I am better off dead than alive!"

But the Lord said: "Are you so very angry?"

Without answering the Lord's question, Jonah went out of

the city and made a booth to shelter him from the heat. The sun was very warm, and the Lord made a wild gourd vine to grow and shelter the angry prophet. Jonah was thankful for the shade of this vine.

To teach Jonah a lesson, God allowed a worm to cut the vine so that it withered. Then the hot winds blew, and the sun beat on Jonah, and again he wished he were dead.

The Lord said: "You have had pity on the gourd, for which you did not toil; nor did you raise it; which grew in a night, and perished in a night! And should not I, indeed, have pity on Nineveh, that great city, in which are more than a hundred and twenty thousand infants, that cannot distinguish between their right hand and their left, and many cattle?"

In this way the prophet from Judah was taught that God loves men of all nations and all races. He was given a wonderful lesson concerning the Father's mercy. God is ready to forgive all who will repent of their sins, if they will turn to Him with all their hearts. Jonah learned, too, that he could never run away from the Lord who sees all that we do and who hears all that we say.

The BOY WHO BECAME KING

"SATURDAY night and nothing to do!" moaned Dick Barrett, slouching on the living-room sofa.

His father looked up from the evening paper and sized up the situation carefully. "No program or party planned for to-night, son?"

"No, dad," replied the youth. "It's getting too close to Christmas vacation, I guess. Everyone has his own plans."

"Where are Roy and Bette?" countered Mr. Barrett.

"Bette's upstairs, I believe, and Roy is down in the playroom splicing some of his motion-picture film."

"What do you suggest, mother?" asked Mr. Barrett, turning to his wife, who had entered the room and had heard the conversation. "Here are three restless young folks looking for action, excitement, and adventure. What can we offer them to make them happy on a Saturday night?"

Bette slipped quietly into the room while her father was speaking, and she joined in the conversation. Before mother could think of an answer the daughter declared: "You are always ready to come to our rescue. What can it be tonight? Ruth Mason is visiting her aunt, and no one else has planned anything. Please help us, mother."

(151)

The Barrett living room was a scene of activity. After the games were finished, the group formed a semi-circle near the fireplace to hear Captain Lane's story.

. WILKE, ARTIST

"Could we have some games and invite Captain and Mrs. Lane over? You always have a good time with them. I'll fix sandwiches, and your father brought a jug of sweet cider home yesterday." Mother Barrett's mind had gone into high gear, and she was planning the evening as she spoke. Dick and Bette snapped at the idea immediately like hungry fish taking bait, and they ran to tell Roy what was in store for them.

"Let's call Sandy Turner and see if he'd like to come over. That will make eight of us for games," suggested Roy, putting up his film-splicing outfit.

"O.K.," agreed Dick. "Mother is calling the Lanes right now."

Two hours later the Barrett living room was a scene of activity. Four alert youngsters, joined by Captain and Mrs. Lane and Dad and Mother Barrett, had finished playing several games. Refreshments were being served by Bette and her mother, and everyone brought his chair into a semicircle facing the crackling logs in the fireplace.

"I was reading in the paper tonight that a group of high-school students will take the place of our city officials for twenty-four hours next Tuesday." Mr. Barrett turned to Captain Lane as he spoke.

"Yes, I know the young fellow who is to act as mayor. He is Robert Tobin, a seventeen-year-old senior." The captain replied between bites of a toasted cheese sandwich.

"It would be fun to be mayor for a while," Dick declared with enthusiasm.

"I'd like the job of chief of police," Sandy Turner suggested.

"They could make me the fire chief," said Roy.

When the boy, Jehoash, was seven years old the high priest presented him to the people and they shouted, "God save the king!

W. WILKE, ARTIST

"Suppose you were President of the United States; what would you do?" asked Mr. Barrett.

"That's too much to imagine," said Roy. "Nobody expects teen-agers to do that."

"No, according to the Constitution you couldn't be President," the captain agreed. "But once there was a boy who became king of a nation when he was much younger than you, Roy," the man added, a faraway look in his eyes.

"Sounds like a story coming up." Bette was serving glasses of cider as she spoke. "We're ready to hear all about it, Captain Tim."

"Now, Timothy, we're not here to listen to stories," Mrs. Lane reminded her husband.

"Oh, yes, we are, Mrs. Lane," said Dick. "We've played games until we're tired. Let's hear a good story."

"This one is exciting, I'll promise you that," began the man. "We'll have to go back some twenty-five hundred years to the little country of Judah."

"It's a Bible story then," whispered Roy to Sandy Turner, who was sitting beside him on the floor near the fireplace.

"There was a queen named Athaliah, the daughter of wicked Jezebel. You will recall that Jezebel was the wife of Ahab and that she threatened to kill Elijah when he destroyed the wicked prophets of Baal. Well, Athaliah was cruel and ruthless like her mother. One of her grandchildren was in line to be king, but this woman decided to have all of her grandchildren murdered so she could hold the throne as queen. When the little princes and princesses were being murdered, a woman snatched up the baby who should rightfully be king and took him and

ROBERTS

"We might have more influence on our world today," declared Roy Barrett, "if the older generation had confidence in us." "It's a big world, though," replied Sandy.

his nurse to the high priest's apartment, which adjoined the Temple of Solomon. The woman who saved the baby was the child's aunt, the wife of the high priest. She hid the little boy for six years in the Temple apartment, and wicked Athaliah had no idea that the royal prince was alive.

"The cruel queen ruled supreme, and, like Jezebel, she made

the people worship idols. There were good people in Judah who longed for a king who would lead them in the way of the true God. This could not happen as long as the cruel queen ruled the nation. Who would overthrow her?

"When the boy, who was named Jehoash, was seven years old, the high priest decided it was time to act. Soldiers were on guard day and night to protect the Temple treasury. One day the priest called a secret meeting of the captains and the soldiers of the Temple. He told them his plan and gave them spears, shields, and other weapons that had been stored in the Temple. Then the high priest brought the boy Jehoash before the soldiers. A crown was placed on his head, and the high priest anointed him king and gave him a copy of God's holy law. The guards shouted: 'God save the king!' "

"Wait until the wicked queen hears about this!" said Bette, who had been listening intently.

"When Athaliah heard the shouting, she hurried to the Temple court. There she saw the boy king standing by a pillar with a crown on his head and all the people shouting with joy. Trumpets were being blown by the guards to honor the new ruler."

"Was this boy the grandson of the wicked queen?" asked Mrs. Barrett.

"That's right," replied the captain. "The queen thought he had been dead almost seven years, yet here he was standing before the people, a king though only a little boy! Now Athaliah knew that the high priest had spared the boy's life. The woman came forward shouting: 'Treason, treason!' But she was the real traitor herself."

"What happened to her?" asked Roy.

"The high priest commanded that the queen be driven from the Temple, and he threatened to kill anyone who would follow her. Then the people rushed to the temple of Baal, wrecked it, and tore down all the heathen images and altars. They had a real house cleaning that day. The wicked queen was killed when she tried to run away. Then the people marched in a parade. They took the boy king to the royal palace, and his uncle, the high priest, was made regent for the kingdom."

"So a seven-year-old boy really became a king of Judah," Dick declared. "What would you do if you were a king, Sandy?"

"That's something to think about. I don't know what I'd do. What kind of king was Jehoash, captain?"

"He started out well enough," continued the storyteller. "The Temple had been neglected for more than a hundred years, and its treasures had been taken away. Since money was needed to repair the temple, the young king had a chest made, and the people brought gifts and put them in it. Workmen repaired the temple, and the priests offered sacrifices. The nation followed in the way of the Lord as long as the high priest lived and counseled the young king.

"When the king did not have this counsel from his uncle, he forgot God and turned to the worship of idols. But he is still remembered as the king, who, as a boy, helped his people keep the commandments of God."

"If young people were given more opportunities under the right guidance and leadership, I believe they could influence our city and national governments more than they do," Mr. Barrett said with emphasis. "They have ideals and lots of enthusiasm."

"Thanks for having confidence in us," Roy exclaimed, going over to his father's chair and putting his hand on the man's shoulder. "Don't you think I'm old enough, dad, to start driving the family car?"

"Not yet, my boy, according to the state laws. You'll have to wait for a beginner's license until you are at least fourteen, and then you can only drive with mother or me. That's to protect you and to safeguard other people on the highway. I'm sure you'll make a good driver when you're old enough to take the wheel."

"Many of the great things of life have been done by young folks," said Captain Lane. The man reached into his pocket and drew out a sheaf of papers. "I found a clipping the other day about what some great men did when they were young. It interested me, so I cut it out and saved it. This says that George Washington surveyed the wilds of Virginia when he was eighteen, and he was an adjutant general with the rank of major at nineteen. Fulton dreamed of his steamboat at fourteen, and Stephenson thought of the locomotive at fifteen. McCormick invented the reaper at twenty-two, and Eli Whitney made his first cotton gin in his early twenties.

"If you're thinking about musicians, Mozart showed his genius at four years of age, while Handel and Rubinstein were prodigies at eight."

"According to that, I guess young folks can do things if they are willing and full of pep," Dick said quickly. "We'll have to get busy, Roy."

"Timothy, have you looked at your watch lately?" asked Mrs. Lane. "Mine tells me that it's after eleven o'clock. We are planning to get up early in the morning and go out to Hillcrest Farm, so I think we'd better start home."

"You're always right, my dear," returned the man. "I feel like staying up hours yet, but in the morning about six thirty I'll wish I had gone to bed earlier. Let's be going. The games and refreshments were wonderful, Mrs. Barrett."

The party broke up with laughter and snatches of chitchat. Dick reminded the captain that he was going to invite them to the farm as soon as he had purchased his new sheep. Bette declared emphatically that she was going to play nursemaid to all the baby lambs when their mothers deserted them.

"By the way," said the captain, as they stood at the door of the Barrett home, "we're going to have a surprise next week, and I know you four young folks will want to come over and see it. I'm as excited about it right now as a boy with a new toy."

"What is it?" exclaimed Bette, clapping her hands.

"Wait and see. It wouldn't be a secret if I told you," returned the man. "We're going now. Good night."

"Captain Tim always keeps us in suspense," said Roy, closing the door. "I wonder what he has up his sleeve this time."

16

An ANGEL DESTROYS the ASSYRIAN ARMY

2 KINGS 18:1 to 20:21

BECAUSE the people of Nineveh believed the message of Jonah and asked God to forgive their sins, their city was spared. Time went by, and the Assyrian empire grew strong and conquered other nations.

Young Prince Hezekiah came to the throne of Judah, the little kingdom in the south of Palestine, at a time when Assyria threatened to attack. When he began to reign at the age of twenty-five he determined to follow the way of the Lord. He destroyed the idols of Baal and opened the temple of the Lord that had been closed for many years. Hezekiah also broke in pieces the bronze serpent that Moses had made to save the people from plague in the wilderness. It seems that the Israelites had offered sacrifices to it and worshiped it during the reign of the evil kings. The Bible declares that King Hezekiah "was loyal to the Lord, he turned not away from following Him, but kept His commands which the Lord had commanded Moses."

When Hezekiah had ruled about four years, the king of Assyria sent his army to attack Samaria, capital of Israel. Soon the city was captured. Ten years later Sennacherib, king of Assyria,

(161)

When Hezekiah prayed, Isaiah answered:
"Therefore thus says the Lord concerning the
king of Assyria: 'He shall not enter this city.' "

W. WILKE, ARTIST

came against Judah and captured some of the cities. Hezekiah remembered what had happened to Israel, so he wrote a letter to the Assyrian ruler, saying: "I have offended; withdraw from me; whatever you lay on me I will bear." Sennacherib required Hezekiah to pay three hundred talents of silver and thirty talents of gold as tribute money. This took so much treasure from the little kingdom that King Hezekiah was forced to remove the silver from the temple and strip the gold from the doors and pillars of that beautiful building.

Soon the Assyrian king decided to capture Judah and take the city of Jerusalem. Sennacherib sent his commander in chief to the capital, and with him went a crafty man named Rabshakeh. This man did his best to discourage the people of Judah and cause them to surrender. To Hezekiah's officers Rabshakeh said: "Say now to Hezekiah, 'Thus says the great king, the king of Assyria: "What confidence is this in which you trust? Do you think that a mere word of the lips is counsel and strength for war? Now in whom do you trust that you have rebelled against me? You have put your trust evidently in the staff of this broken reed, Egypt, on which if a man lean, it will run into his hand and pierce it. . . . Now have I come up against this place to destroy it without the Lord's approval? The Lord Himself said to me, 'Go up against this land and destroy it.' " ' "

Rabshakeh also spoke to the men of Judah, but they refused to answer the enemy. As soon as King Hezekiah heard what the Assyrians were doing, he tore his garments, covered himself with sackcloth, and went to the temple to pray. The king also sent a messenger to Isaiah, asking him to pray for the nation.

The brave prophet sent this message of courage back to King Hezekiah: "Thus says the Lord: 'Do not be afraid of the words that you have heard, with which the menials of the king of Assyria have blasphemed Me. Behold, I will put a spirit in him, so that when he hears a certain rumor he shall return to his own land, and I will cause him to fall by the sword in his own land.'"

Soon after this, Rabshakeh returned to the king of Assyria and told him how the men of Judah had refused to surrender. This caused Sennacherib to write an insulting letter to Hezekiah. When the king of Judah received it, he went again to the temple and spread the message out before the Lord and prayed: "O Lord, the God of Israel, who art seated upon the cherubim, Thou art God, even Thou alone, over all the kingdoms of the earth; Thou hast made the heavens and the earth. Incline Thine ear, O Lord, and hear; open Thine eyes, O Lord, and see, and hear all the words of Sennacherib, which he has sent to insult the living God. Of a truth, O Lord, the kings of Assyria have laid waste the nations and their land, and have cast their gods into the fire, for they were no gods, but the work of men's hands, wood and stone; and so they have destroyed them. But now, O Lord our God, deliver us from his hand, that all the kingdoms of the earth may know that Thou, O Lord, art God alone."

While Hezekiah prayed, Isaiah, the prophet, sent him this answer from the Lord: "Therefore thus says the Lord concerning the king of Assyria: 'He shall not enter this city, or shoot an arrow there; neither shall he come before it with shield, or cast up a mound against it. By the way that he came, by the same shall he return; but he shall not enter this city,' is the Lord's oracle."

That night the angel of the Lord went through the army of the Assyrians as it was camped near Jerusalem and slew 185,000 of the enemy. The next morning the men of Judah found the dead lying in the camp. The king of Assyria had fled back to Nineveh, taking with him the handful of men who remained.

This great victory has been described by the poet:

"The Assyrian came down like a wolf on the fold,
  And his cohorts were gleaming in purple and gold;
  And the sheen of their spears was like stars on the sea,
  When the blue wave rolls nightly on deep Galilee.

"Like the leaves of the forest when summer is green,
  That host with their banners at sunset were seen:
  Like the leaves of the forest when autumn hath blown,
  That host on the morrow lay withered and strown.

"For the Angel of Death spread his wings on the blast,
  And breathed in the face of the foe as he passed;
  And the eyes of the sleepers waxed deadly and chill,
  And their hearts but once heaved, and forever grew still!

"And there lay the steed with his nostril all wide,
  But through it there rolled not the breath of his pride;
  And the foam of his gasping lay white on the turf,
  And cold as the spray of the rock-beating surf.

"And there lay the rider distorted and pale,
  With the dew on his brow, and the rust on his mail:
  And the tents were all silent, the banners alone,
  The lances unlifted, the trumpet unblown.

"And the widows of Ashur are loud in their wail,
  And the idols are broke in the temple of Baal;
  And the might of the Gentile, unsmote by the sword,
  Hath melted like snow in the glance of the Lord!"

                    —*Lord Byron.*

King Hezekiah watched the sundial. True enough, the shadow was moving backward.
One, two, five degrees. Then back ten full degrees! The Lord had heard his prayer!

Thus the message of God's prophet came true, and Judah was saved from destruction.

Now in those days Hezekiah took suddenly ill with a severe abscess or boil. Isaiah, the prophet, visited the ruler and said: "Thus says the Lord: 'Set your house in order for you shall die and not live.'"

Hezekiah was heartbroken. He turned his face to the wall and wept. He prayed to the Lord, saying: "Remember now, O Lord, I pray Thee, how I have walked before Thee in truth and sincerity of heart, and have done that which was good in Thy sight."

Isaiah left the king's bedroom; but while he was walking through the courtyard, another message came to him from God.

King Hezekiah was proud to have officers from far-off Babylon visit him. He took them into his treasure house and showed them his silver, gold, spices, fine oil, and weapons.

The prophet was given this instruction: "Return and say to Hezekiah, the prince of My people, 'Thus says the Lord, the God of David your father: "I have heard your prayer, I have seen your tears; see, I will heal you; on the third day you shall go up to the house of the Lord. I will also add fifteen more years to your life, and I will deliver you and this city from the hand of the king of Assyria, and I will defend this city for My own sake and for the sake of My servant David." ' "

Isaiah also gave the king special treatment for the infection. "Let them take a cake of figs," said the prophet, "and place it upon the boil that he may recover."

The king longed to know for certain that he would get well and live for fifteen years. He said to Isaiah, "What will be the sign that the Lord will heal me, and that I shall go up to the house of the Lord the third day?"

"This will be the sign to you from the Lord, that the Lord will do the thing that He has promised," said Isaiah. "Shall the shadow go forward ten steps, or back ten steps?"

Hezekiah said: "It is easy for the shadow to go forward ten steps; rather let the shadow turn back ten steps."

King Hezekiah watched the sundial carefully. True enough, the shadow was moving backward. One, two, five degrees. Then back ten full degrees! How it was done we do not know, for only the God of heaven could perform this miracle. The king rejoiced when he saw the shadow move backward, for he knew that the Lord had answered his prayer.

Now the king of Babylon in his palace on the Euphrates River heard that Hezekiah had recovered from his serious sickness. The Babylonian ruler sent messengers to Jerusalem with a present for the king of Judah. King Hezekiah was proud to have officers from the far-off empire visit him. He took them into his treasure house and showed them his silver, gold, spices, fine oil, and all his weapons of war.

The king missed a golden opportunity to tell these pagan messengers of the God who created the heavens and the earth. He could have related to them the wonderful story of how he had been healed of his illness. Instead, pride and vanity ruled the king's heart, and the messengers went back to Babylon to tell their sovereign of the riches the little kingdom of Judah possessed.

Isaiah stood before Hezekiah and reproved him for his folly. The prophet said: "Behold, days are coming when all that is in your house and that which your fathers have stored up to this day shall be carried away to Babylon; nothing shall be left." The prophet continued: "Also some of your sons who shall be your issue, whom you shall beget, they shall take, and they shall become eunuchs in the palace of the king of Babylon."

"Good is the word of the Lord which you have spoken," said Hezekiah. He knew he had made a mistake, but he was thankful the enemy would not come against Judah during his lifetime.

Captain Tim's Bible Quiz

To prove to her teacher that she had been reading the Bible stories, Bette made out a group of twenty questions. When Miss Mason had gone over the questions, she declared that she could answer three fourths of them correctly. Can you score 100 per cent on this test? You will find the correct answers on pages 252, 253.

1. Who was the crippled son of Jonathan that David showed special kindness to by calling him to live at the royal court?
2. What prophet of God reproved David for his sin?
3. In what position did Joab serve David?
4. On what mountain did the prophet Elijah make the test between the true God and the heathen idol, Baal?
5. In what city did King Ahab have his palace?
6. Which of David's sons tried to steal the throne from his father?
7. When Solomon became king, for what did he pray?
8. How long did David reign as king of Israel?
9. What queen from Ethiopia came to visit King Solomon?
10. Who was plowing in the field when he saw the prophet Elijah and left his work to follow the man of God?
11. What did the ravens bring to Elijah while he was hiding?
12. What wicked queen threatened to kill Elijah?
13. What important piece of equipment did one of the sons of the prophets lose in the river?
14. Who was the king of Tyre that helped Solomon build the temple?
15. What city did Jonah save by preaching God's message?
16. What Syrian general was cured of leprosy through the faithfulness of a captive maid?
17. What messenger ran to David, but when he stood before the ruler had no news to tell the king?
18. What happened to the Syrian army so that Elisha was able to lead them in a helpless condition to the king of Israel?
19. Who was the mother of Solomon?
20. What did Solomon have brought by ship from distant lands?

A PROPHET FACES DEATH

JEREMIAH 1:1 to 36:32

JOSIAH, the great-grandson of Hezekiah, came to the throne of Judah when he was only eight years of age. At the same time another youth named Jeremiah was growing up in the village of Anathoth, three miles northeast of Jerusalem. This boy was to live to see the rise of the Babylonian Empire and the end of Egypt's power. He was also to witness the destruction of his own country, for in his lifetime he was to see fierce and cruel enemies marching and remarching across Judah, ravaging the land, and destroying its cities.

Jeremiah was a quiet, tenderhearted youth of the tribe of Levi, trained like Samuel before him to be a priest. He knew the sad history of how his nation had been brought low by the wickedness of King Manasseh and King Amon, who had caused the people to worship idols. Jeremiah was happy to see the new day when young King Josiah turned the people back to the worship of the true God.

The king repaired the temple of the Lord, and while this work was going on, a scroll was discovered which contained a copy of the law. This was read to King Josiah, and he was shocked to learn how far the nation had drifted from God. When the scribe had finished reading the law, Josiah said: "Go, inquire of the Lord for me and for the people and for all Judah, concerning the words of this book that has been found; for great is the wrath of the Lord that is kindled against us, because our fathers have not listened to the words of this book, to conform to all that is written in it concerning us."

The king gathered all the elders of the land together, and he read the words of the law in their hearing. Then he made a covenant with the Lord to walk in the commandments and to keep the statutes, and all the people pledged themselves to obey God's commands. The altars to pagan gods were broken down, and idol worship was abolished throughout the nation.

In the thirteenth year of King Josiah, God called the young Jeremiah to the difficult task of reproving the people for their sins. When called to give the message of repentance, he said: "Ah, Lord God! I cannot speak; for I am only a youth."

But the Lord said: "Do not say, 'I am only a youth'; for to all to whom I send you shall you go, and all that I command you shall you speak. Do not be afraid of them; for I am with you to deliver you."

Then the hand of the Lord touched the young man's mouth, and God said: "See! I put My words in your mouth; this day I give you authority over the nations and kingdoms, to root up and to pull down, to wreck and to ruin, to build and to plant."

Jeremiah was told to go to the cities and talk to the crowds in the market places and in the streets. He must warn them that if they continued in their rebellious ways the nation would be destroyed. The young prophet gave the message, but most of the people refused to listen. Then the Lord gave Jeremiah a picture of the doom that was certain to come upon Judah.

He was told how a mighty enemy would come down from the north and overthrow the cities and destroy the temple. Because the people would not obey the commands of God they would be taken into exile as slaves of an enemy king.

Again the nation refused to listen to the warnings, and when King Josiah died many of the people turned upon Jeremiah and called him a traitor because he had warned of trouble to come.

Jehoahaz, the son of Josiah, had reigned but three months when Necho, king of Egypt, came up against Jerusalem and took the king a prisoner and placed Jehoiakim, another son of Josiah, on the throne, ordering him to pay immense tribute as a vassal.

It was in this crisis that Jeremiah went to the court of the temple to warn the people of approaching doom. The Lord said to the prophet: "Stand in the court of the house of the Lord, and speak to all the people of Judah who come to worship in the house of the Lord all the words that I command you to speak to them; keep not back one word! Perhaps they may listen, and turn each from his evil way, so that I may repent of the evil which I am planning to bring upon them because of their evil doings."

When the priests and prophets heard the words that Jeremiah spoke, they became angry. After he had finished speaking, they grabbed him and said: "You shall die! How dare you prophesy in the name of the Lord, saying, 'This house shall become like Shiloh, and this city shall become an uninhabited waste'?"

Soon a mob crowded around Jeremiah, and when the princes of Judah heard what was happening they came from the palace and took their seats at the new gate at the entrance of the temple. The priests and prophets shouted to the rulers, saying: "This man deserves to die; for he has prophesied against this city in the terms which you have heard."

As the angry mob shouted for Jeremiah's death and it seemed that he had only a few moments to live, the brave prophet never flinched from his duty. He turned to the princes and made a bold appeal, saying: "The Lord sent me to prophesy against this house and this city all the words which you have heard. But now, if you amend your ways and your doings, and listen to the voice of the Lord your God, the Lord will repent of the evil which He has pronounced against you. As for myself, see! I am in your hands. Do to me as you think right and proper. Only be well assured of this, that, if you put me to death, you will be bringing innocent blood upon yourselves, upon this city, and upon its people; for the Lord has truly sent me to you, to speak all these words in your hearing."

A silence fell upon the throng. Then the princes and all the people shouted to the priests, saying: "This man does not deserve to die; for he has spoken to us in the name of the Lord our God." In this moment the angry crowd sided with Jeremiah, and he was saved from death.

Some of the elders came forward and spoke to the people. They reminded them that in the days of King Hezekiah, a prophet of the Lord had given severe messages to the nation, but he had not been put to death. "Did Hezekiah king of Judah and all the people of Judah go to the length of putting him to death?" they asked. "Did they not rather reverence the Lord, and entreat the favor of the Lord, so that the Lord re-

The enemies of Jeremiah had the proph
imprisoned and placed in stocks; but ev
in the dungeon he gave God's messag

STANDARD PUB. (

pented of the evil which He had pronounced against them? We, on the contrary, are in the act of bringing great evil upon ourselves."

While Jeremiah was saved, another prophet named Urijah, who also prophesied the same message from the Lord, did not escape the anger of the king. Although this second prophet escaped to Egypt, officers of Jehoiakim followed him and brought him back to Jerusalem and he was imprisoned and finally put to death.

Friends of Jeremiah saved him in the hour of danger. They loved him and guarded him. Ahikam, a special friend of Jeremiah's, gave shelter to the prophet and protected him from the angry mobs in time of danger.

Although Jeremiah's enemies were unable to kill him, they brought so much pressure to bear on the government authorities that at last the prophet was imprisoned and placed in stocks. Even in the dungeon Jeremiah did not give up the task of speaking God's message. He said: "It is in my heart like a burning fire, shut up in my bones; I am worn out with holding it in—I cannot endure it."

The time came when the Lord told Jeremiah to write a last warning to Judah on a scroll. The prophet called Baruch, a young friend who acted as his secretary, and he dictated the message to him. Then Jeremiah said unto Baruch: "Go you, then, and from the scroll which you have written at my dictation read the words of the Lord in the hearing of the people gathered in the house of the Lord on a fast day, as well as in the hearing of all Judah who come from their cities. Perhaps, as they present their supplication before the Lord, they will turn each from his

As Jehudi read a portion of the prophet's message, the king would cut it from the scroll and toss it into the flames

STANDARD PUB. CO

evil way, when they realize how great is the anger and fury which the Lord has expressed against this people."

Baruch followed the instructions of Jeremiah and read the words of the Lord upon a festal day when the temple was thronged with people. Now Michaiah, the grandson of Shaphan, saw what was happening and hurried off to the palace to tell the officials. The officers instantly sent for Baruch and ordered him to bring the scroll to the palace. So Baruch came before the king's officers and sat down as he was commanded. When the officers heard the words of Jeremiah, they were afraid and looked at one another anxiously. They knew they must give a report of this matter to the king.

"Pray, tell us! How did you write all these words? Was it at his dictation?" they asked Baruch.

"Yes!" answered Baruch, telling of Jeremiah's message. "He dictated all these words to me, and I wrote them with ink on the scroll." Then the king's officers, who wished to be friendly, said: "Go into hiding, you and Jeremiah, and let no one know where you are."

Baruch hurried away, leaving the scroll with the king's officers, and they reported the whole matter to King Jehoiakim, and Jehudi read Jeremiah's message to the king. Now it was in the ninth month, and the king was living in his winter house. A fire was burning in the room to give warmth. As Jehudi read a portion of the scroll, the king would cut it off with his penknife and toss it into the flames. Part by part, as it was read, God's message was thrown into the fire and consumed.

King Jehoiakim and his wicked followers were not afraid of the divine warnings, neither did they repent of their sins.

After the message had been read, the king ordered the arrest of Baruch, the secretary, and of Jeremiah, the prophet; but these faithful men could not be found, for the Lord had hidden them.

Then God spoke again to the prophet Jeremiah, saying: "Take another scroll, and write on it all the words that were on the first scroll, which Jehoiakim, the king of Judah, burned."

In this second message Jeremiah gave more fearful warnings of the doom that was coming upon the wicked nation. In this way the Lord tried again and again to turn the people of Judah from their evil ways and to save them from destruction at the hand of their enemies; but they would not heed the divine warnings.

18

JERUSALEM FALLS to the ARMY of BABYLON

JEREMIAH 37:1 to 52:34

THE day came, as Jeremiah had predicted, when Nebuchadnezzar, king of Babylon, sent his armies against Judah and compelled King Jehoiakim to pay tribute as a vassal king. After three years of this bondage, King Jehoiakim thought that he was strong enough to rebel against the Babylonian rule, but his plans failed. Soon King Jehoiakim died, and his eighteen-year-old son, Jehoiachin, came to the throne. The young king reigned only three months, however, before Nebuchadnezzar came against Jerusalem with a stronger army and captured it.

When King Jehoiachin surrendered, it was a sorry day for the royal family. The king's mother, his wives, his nobles, and his officers became captives of Nebuchadnezzar and, with ten thousand Jewish soldiers and many of the best people of Judah, were carried away to the city of Babylon. Then King Nebuchadnezzar made King Jehoiachin's uncle, Zedekiah, ruler of the captive kingdom.

About this time the Babylonian, or Chaldean, army withdrew from the city of Jerusalem because the armies of Egypt

(181)

When the city of Jerusalem fell to the king of Babylon, the priests left the beautiful temple, and the sacred services were discontinued.

were advancing to the north. Jeremiah the prophet attempted to leave Jerusalem to visit his estate, but at the city gate a sentry arrested him, saying: "You are deserting to the Chaldeans."

"It is false; I am not deserting," said Jeremiah.

However, the sentry would not listen to the prophet, but arrested him and brought him before the king's officers. The officers were so angry with the prophet that they beat him and put him in prison, and he remained there many days. During this time he constantly said that the Babylonian army would return and again lay siege to Jerusalem. The day came when the enemy returned and surrounded the city. Then King Zedekiah sent for Jeremiah and asked him secretly: "Is there any word from the Lord?"

"There is," answered Jeremiah. "You shall be given into the hand of the king of Babylon."

This made the king very angry, and he sent Jeremiah back to the prison and ordered him to be given a loaf of bread each day as long as there was any food in the city. Since the Babylonian army had surrounded Jerusalem, food was becoming very scarce.

The situation grew worse in the city as famine and disease broke out among the people. Jeremiah warned the citizens: "Thus says the Lord: 'He who remains in this city shall die by sword, famine, and pestilence; but he who surrenders to the Chaldeans shall have his life given to him as a prize of war.' For thus says the Lord: 'This city shall certainly be given into the hand of the king of Babylon's army, and they shall take it.' "

When the princes heard this, they rushed to the king and cried: "Pray, have this man put to death; for he is disheartening the soldiers that are left in this city, and all the people as well, by addressing such words to them; for this man is seeking not the welfare of this people, but their ruin."

"See! he is in your hand," said King Zedekiah.

The princes took Jeremiah and threw him into a cistern which was in the court of the prison. The water had been drawn out of the cistern, leaving it filled with filthy mire. Jeremiah sank down into the mud, and he would have starved to death had not a friend, Ebedmelech, an Ethiopian servant in the palace, come to his rescue. When this man heard that Jeremiah had been put in the cistern, he went straight to the king and said: "My lord the king, these men have done wrong in treating Jeremiah as they have done, casting him into the cistern, to die where he is of famine, because there is no more bread in the city."

The king was touched at the courage of this servant, and he ordered three men to rescue Jeremiah. With the aid of Ebedmelech the men went to the cistern, let down some old rags, which Jeremiah could put under his armpits, and drew him up out of the filth.

Once more King Zedekiah sent for Jeremiah and asked him to tell the truth concerning the future of the country. Jeremiah said to the king: "If I tell you the truth, are you not sure to put me to death?"

King Zedekiah swore an oath in secret that he would protect the prophet from all harm. Then Jeremiah made a final appeal to the king to end the fight. He told the ruler that if he would surrender, he would be saved; but if he held out against the enemy, he would not escape death. Jeremiah said: "If you do not surrender to the officers of the king of Babylon, this city shall be handed over to the Chaldeans, who shall burn it; and you yourself shall not escape from their hand."

The king was weak, however, and could not stand against his nobles. Therefore, he refused to surrender, and the enemy made the final fierce attack. The walls of the city were broken down, and the soldiers swarmed into the palace. King Zedekiah fled, but was captured. His two sons were slain, and the king was blinded and taken in chains to Babylon, where he remained a prisoner until he died.

The walls of Jerusalem were broken down, and Solomon's Temple and the king's palace were destroyed. Many of the other beautiful buildings in the city were burned with fire.

Now the Babylonian captain in command of the city treated Jeremiah kindly. The prophet was released from prison, and the captain said to him: "Now, see! I release you this day from the chains that are upon your hands. If you are disposed to come with me to Babylon, come, and I will look well after you; but if you are not disposed to come with me to Babylon, think no more of it. See! the whole land is before you. Go wherever you think right and proper." Jeremiah decided to stay in the land of Judah and live among the poor who had been left behind when thousands were carried captive to Babylon.

Strife broke out between ambitious men in Judah and the king of Ammon, who lived beyond Jordan. The situation became so desperate that many of the Jews who remained in the land decided to seek refuge in Egypt. Jeremiah sought the Lord for instruction, and the word came that they should not go to Egypt. However, the people refused to accept his message, and a large caravan set forth on the road toward the land of the Nile.

They took Jeremiah and Baruch with them, even though these men went against their will.

Through more than forty years Jeremiah was a faithful prophet of God. Although his messages were hated and scorned, although the kings and people refused to obey the word of the Lord, this courageous man stood true and loyal in every crisis. The word of the Lord was in him as a burning fire, and he could not be silent when he had a message to give.

19

The KING WHO FORGOT HIS DREAM

DANIEL 1:1 to 2:49

THE predictions that Isaiah and Jeremiah made concerning the fall of Jerusalem came to pass. In the last years of the kingdom of Judah the rulers were weak, evil men who disobeyed the commands of the Lord. Finally, Nebuchadnezzar, king of Babylon, came with his army and captured Jerusalem. The city was left in ruins when the soldiers carried thousands of citizens off as prisoners.

Among the captives taken to Babylon from Judah were four young men of royal blood. They were strong and handsome, skillful and capable of learning. Daniel was the name of the youth who seems to have been the leader of the group. He and his three companions were taken to the royal palace at Babylon. His name was changed to Belteshazzar, and his three friends were given the names Shadrach, Meshach, and Abednego.

These youth had grown up in Judean homes where they had been taught of the true God; they had gone to Solomon's temple to worship the Lord who made heaven and earth. Now they suddenly found themselves in a heathen land where pagan idols were worshiped and strange rites and ceremonies were per-

(187)

You, O king, looked, and lo! there was a
great image," the Hebrew youth, Daniel,
declared to the amazed Nebuchadnezzar.

The officer allowed the young men to eat simple, wholesome food. After ten days they were better in appearance and fatter than the others who ate from the king's table.

formed. The four young princes determined that they would be true to God in every test they faced.

The first problem that came to them was concerning their food. Ashpenaz, the king's officer in charge of the four Hebrews, brought them special food and wine from the king's table. Now, the young men had been taught to eat food that was "clean" according to the law of Moses. They knew also that some of this food had been offered to idols, and to eat it would mean that they were honoring heathen gods.

Ashpenaz liked Daniel, and when the youth came to the officer with the request not to be served the king's dainties, the man listened with sympathy. But he said to Daniel: "I am afraid of my lord, the king, who has assigned your food and your drink, lest he find you looking more haggard than the youths of your own age, in which case you would forfeit my head to the king."

"Pray, try your servants for ten days," said Daniel, "letting us have vegetables to eat, and water to drink; then compare our appearance with the appearance of the youths who eat of the king's delicacies, and deal with your servants in accordance with what you see."

The officer agreed to this test, and he allowed the young men to eat simple, wholesome food. At the end of ten days they were better in appearance and fatter than the other young men who ate the food from the king's table. After that the officer allowed these princes to have a simple diet of vegetables as their regular fare. Daniel and his companions were trained in the king's school, and in the examination at the end of their course of study they were found wiser than the magicians and astrologers of Babylon.

One night King Nebuchadnezzar had a dream. When he awoke he could not remember his dream, and he was perplexed. He commanded his magicians and enchanters to stand before him and describe what he had dreamed.

"O king, live forever! Tell your servants the dream, and we will give the interpretation," begged the wise men.

But the king was unable to tell his dream. He said: "I am fully resolved that, if you do not make known to me the dream and its interpretation, you shall be hewn limb from limb, and your houses shall be made a dunghill. But if you tell me the dream and its interpretation, you shall receive from me gifts and rewards and great honor. So tell me the dream and its interpretation."

Again the wise men asked the king to reveal his dream, and then they would give him the meaning of it. The magicians realized that they were in a hopeless position. They said: "There is not a man on the earth who can tell the king what he asks; for no king, however great and mighty, has asked such a thing of any magician, enchanter, or Chaldean. The king is asking a hard thing, and none can tell the king what he asks, except the gods whose dwelling is not with mortal flesh."

King Nebuchadnezzar was furious. He commanded that all the wise men of Babylon be killed. This meant that Daniel and his three friends would die, for they were classed with the wise men.

Daniel and his companions had not been called before the king with the wise men. Therefore when the soldiers came to kill them, Daniel asked what the swift punishment was all about. "Why is the king's decree so harsh?" Daniel asked.

When the officers explained the reason, Daniel went to the king and asked that time be granted so that he might tell him the meaning of his dream.

Then Daniel hurried home and told Shadrach, Meshach, and Abednego what had happened. The four young men prayed earnestly, and God revealed the dream to Daniel.

The next morning Daniel went to the officer of the guard and pleaded with him not to kill any of the wise men. "Do not destroy the wise men of Babylon," he said; "bring me before the king, that I may give the king the interpretation."

The officer proudly hurried Daniel to the palace and told King Nebuchadnezzar that he had a man who could reveal the forgotten dream.

I see four men loose, walking in
e midst of the fire," shouted King
ebuchadnezzar to his ministers.

WILKE, ARTIST

Daniel went to the officer of the guard and pleaded with him. "Do not destroy the wise men of Babylon; bring me before the king, that I may give the king the interpretation."

"Are you able to make known to me the dream that I have seen, and its interpretation?" asked the king in astonishment and wonder.

Daniel humbly replied: "No wise men, enchanters, magicians, or astrologers are able to tell the king the secret which the king has asked; but there is a God in the heavens who reveals secrets, and He makes known to King Nebuchadnezzar what shall be in the end of the days."

In this way Daniel refused to take any honor to himself; he gave God the full credit for revealing the dream to him. Then with courage to believe that he had been given the king's dream, the Hebrew youth declared:

"You, O king, looked, and lo! there was a great image. This

image, which was of vast size and surpassing brightness, stood before you; and its appearance was terrible. As for that image, its head was of fine gold, its breast and arms were of silver, its belly and thighs of bronze, its legs of iron, its feet partly of iron, and partly of clay. You looked till you saw a stone hewn from a mountain without hands, which smote the image on its feet of iron and clay, breaking them in pieces. Then the iron, the clay, the bronze, the silver, and the gold were broken in pieces together, and became like chaff from summer threshing floors, and were carried away by the wind, so that no trace of them could be found; while the stone that smote the image became a great mountain, filling all the earth. This was the dream, and we will tell the king the interpretation of it."

Without pausing for an answer from the king, Daniel gave the meaning of the dream. He told Nebuchadnezzar that his kingdom was the head of gold, and that other empires would follow Babylon. Today, in the light of history, we know that the silver of the image represented Medo-Persia, the brass was Greece, and the iron represented the empire of Rome. The mixture of iron and clay stands for the divided condition of the nations in Europe as they are at the present time. Daniel declared that in the days of the iron and clay, "the God of the heavens shall set up a kingdom which shall never be destroyed, nor shall the kingdom be left to another people."

The king was convinced that Daniel had spoken the truth. He came down from his throne and bowed humbly before the Hebrew youth, saying: "Truly, your God is the God of gods, and the Lord of kings; and He is a revealer of secrets, inasmuch as you have been able to reveal this secret."

20

A FIERY FURNACE and an INSANE KING

DANIEL 3:1 to 4:37

King Nebuchadnezzar must have remembered his dream of the great metal image. He was not satisfied, however, for Babylon to be the head of gold; he wanted his empire to stand forever. Therefore he had a giant image more than a hundred feet tall set up on the plain of Dura. It was covered entirely with gold. This image was no doubt set up to show the monarch's desire to challenge the idea that Babylon might someday fall.

The king sent for all his governors, judges, counselors, and other high officials to come from all the provinces for the dedication of the golden image. On the day set for the celebration a vast throng of people assembled on the plain of Dura. The herald shouted King Nebuchadnezzar's instructions to the crowd, saying: "To you is given a command, O peoples, nations, and tongues, that as soon as you hear the sound of the horn, the pipe, the lyre, the trigon, the harp, the bagpipe, and every other kind of musical instrument, you shall fall down and prostrate yourselves before the image of gold which King Nebuchadnezzar has set up; and whoever does not fall down and prostrate himself shall forthwith be cast into the midst of a furnace of flaming fire."

As soon as the throng heard the music, all the people of every nation and language bowed before the golden image, as the king had commanded.

No, not everyone bowed! Three young government officials refused to worship the pagan idol. They were Shadrach, Meshach, and Abednego. No doubt Daniel would have stood with his companions, but he was evidently not at the celebration. As soon as the Babylonians saw the three men standing, they hurried to Nebuchadnezzar and said: "Now there are certain Jews whom you have appointed in charge of the affairs of the province of Babylon, Shadrach, Meshach, and Abednego; these men, O king, pay no regard to you; they do not serve your gods, nor do they prostrate themselves before the image of gold which you have set up."

The king's anger was terrible. He commanded the three Hebrews to be brought before him, and with fury in his eyes he said: "Is it true, O Shadrach, Meshach, and Abednego, that you do not serve my gods, nor prostrate yourselves before the image of gold which I have set up?" Nebuchadnezzar went on to say that he would give them another chance to bow before the image, and if they did not do as he had commanded, he would have them cast into the furnace of flaming fire.

"O Nebuchadnezzar, we need not waste words in discussing this matter with you," said the three brave men. "If our God, whom we serve, is able to deliver us, He will deliver us out of the furnace of flaming fire, and out of your hand, O king; but even if not, be it known to you, O king, we will not serve your gods, nor prostrate ourselves before the image of gold which you have set up."

When Nebuchadnezzar heard this straightforward reply, he was furious, and his face was distorted with rage against the three princes who refused to bow at his command. He ordered the furnace to be heated seven times hotter than usual. Then he commanded certain of his strongest soldiers to bind the three officials and throw them into the fiery furnace. The three Hebrews fell down in the midst of the fire. The furnace was so hot that the soldiers who threw the men into the fire were killed by the terrific heat.

King Nebuchadnezzar watched for a moment, and then he became alarmed. He called his ministers and asked: "Did we not cast three men bound into the midst of the fire?"

"Certainly, O king," they answered.

"Well, I see four men loose," shouted the king, "walking in the midst of the fire, quite unscathed; and the appearance of the fourth resembles one of the gods."

Then King Nebuchadnezzar edged close to the furnace and called out: "O Shadrach, Meshach, and Abednego, servants of the most high God, come out, and come here!"

The three Hebrews walked out of the furnace, and the amazed officials and the king saw that the fire had not burned them or even singed their hair. There was no smell of smoke or fire upon their clothing.

King Nebuchadnezzar was ready to give the God of heaven praise for protecting the three Hebrews. "Blessed be the God of Shadrach, Meshach, and Abednego, who has sent His angel to deliver His servants who trusted in Him, and frustrated the

In selfish boasting the king exclaimed as he walked on the roof of his palace: "Is not this great Babylon, which I have built as a royal residence, by my own mighty power?"

king's order, by surrendering their own persons, rather than serve and worship any god, except their own God! Therefore I make a decree that any people, nation, or tongue, that speaks a word against the God of Shadrach, Meshach, and Abednego, shall be hewn limb from limb, and their houses made a dunghill; for there is no other god who is able to deliver in this manner." Then the king promoted Shadrach, Meshach, and Abednego and gave them more responsibility in the kingdom.

Nebuchadnezzar was so impressed by the power and greatness of God in caring for His children, that he sent a message to all the people of his kingdom saying: "Peace be multiplied to you! It is my pleasure to tell of the signs and wonders that the most high God has wrought toward me.

"How great are His signs,
And how mighty His wonders!
His kingdom is an everlasting kingdom,
And His dominion endures throughout the ages."

Nebuchadnezzar had another dream, and he summoned Daniel to reveal its meaning. The king told how he saw a giant tree. It was so tall and its branches were so widespread that the beasts of the field rested in its shade and the birds rested in its branches.

While the king watched the tree in his dream, he heard a voice from heaven saying:

"Hew down the tree, and lop off its branches,
Shake off its leaves, and scatter its fruit;
Drive away the beasts from under its shadow,
And the birds from among its branches.
Yet leave the stump of its roots in the earth,
Secured by a band of iron and bronze,
Among the tender grass of the field;
Let him be drenched by the dew of the heavens,
And let him have his share with the beasts of the field;
Let his mind be changed from a man's,
And the mind of a beast be given to him,
And let seven years pass over him."

When Daniel heard the dream, he was stunned. He did not know what to say. The king saw the amazed look on the man's face, and he said: "Let not the dream and its interpretation upset you!"

"My lord," replied Daniel, "may the dream be for those who hate you, and its interpretation for your enemies! The tree which you saw, which grew great and strong; whose height reached to the heavens, and its bound of vision to the very end of the earth; whose leaves were fair, and whose fruit was abundant, providing food for all; under whose shadow the beasts of the field were sheltering, and among whose branches the birds of the air were nestling—it is yourself, O king, who have grown so great and strong, that your greatness reaches to the heavens, and your dominion to the very end of the earth. And as the king saw a guardian, a holy one, coming down from the heavens, and saying, 'Hew down the tree, and destroy it.'" Daniel went on to tell the king that in the same way the tree was cut down, so he would lose his mind, and in his madness he would go out into the fields and eat grass like an ox. For seven years he would be in this state of insanity.

Daniel pleaded with the king to love and serve God. "Therefore, O king," said Daniel, "be pleased to accept my advice, and break off your sins by practicing almsgiving, and your guilt by showing mercy to the poor; then perhaps your prosperity may be prolonged."

A year later the king was walking on the roof of his palace surveying the great city of many wonders. In selfish boasting, he exclaimed: "Is not this great Babylon, which I have built as a royal residence, by my own mighty power, and for my own glorious majesty?"

While he was yet speaking he became insane, and he wandered in the fields like an animal. When seven years had passed, his reason returned. Then Nebuchadnezzar blessed the God of heaven and said:

"For His dominion is an everlasting dominion,
And His kingdom endures throughout the ages."

TELEVISION *in* ANCIENT BABYLON

ONE evening, almost a week after Captain Lane had mentioned "surprise" to Dick, Bette, and Roy, a telephone call brought an invitation from Mrs. Lane for the trio to come over and help solve the mystery.

"What are we waiting for?" called Roy as soon as Bette told him the news. "Come on, Dick, let's see what Captain Tim's surprise is."

"I'll be with you as soon as I grab my jacket," replied Dick, coming to the door of his room. "Don't want my sniffles to turn into a bad cold."

"We're going to see Captain and Mrs. Lane for a little while, mother," said Bette, "if it's all right with you."

"Yes, dear," called mother from the sewing room. "Don't stay too long, however. Remember you have studying to do."

"Thanks," returned the daughter. "We'll not forget."

The trio of juniors hurried down the walk and across the street to the Lane residence. "Don't run, Roy, the surprise will wait," urged Bette who was doing her best to keep up with her brothers.

(201)

es," said Captain Lane, "we have been thinking
getting a television set for some time. This is our
ristmas present a couple of weeks in advance."

WILKE, ARTIST

"Go right into the study," Mrs. Lane said as she greeted her visitors at the door. Captain Lane's study was a familiar retreat for the Barretts. They had spent many hours there chatting with their friend, listening to his stories, and seeking his help in solving their problems. The captain was standing in front of a beautiful mahogany cabinet, hands in his pockets, a broad grin on his face.

"Look, it's a new television set!" exclaimed Bette.

"There's a basketball game on the screen. Is this fun!" Roy hurried forward to stand by his friends.

"Boy, is this a surprise!" said Dick gaily.

"Ha! You remembered, did you, Dick? Yes, we have been thinking of getting a television set for some time. This is our Christmas present a couple of weeks in advance. Look at that shot." The man talked excitedly as he watched the university teams playing in the campus gymnasium miles away.

"Television seems more wonderful than radio," said Bette, sitting down in an easy chair where she could watch the screen.

"It is more wonderful," Dick assured his sister. "Look, the score is 38-34. It's a close game."

"Sit down, boys," suggested the captain. "I forgot my manners in all the excitement."

For some fifteen minutes an interested group watched the television screen. When the game ended with a victory for State, the man snapped the switch, turning off the set. "It's a day of marvels, isn't it?"

"Who would have imagined twenty-five years ago that we could see things going on hundreds of miles away the moment they happened?" Mrs. Lane declared.

Only the walls and foundations remain of Nebuchadnezzar's great Babylon, a city three and a half miles long by three miles wide, protected by a wall and huge gates.

"I suppose the next thing they will try to do is to get pictures of what is coming before it happens," said Bette, laughing at her fantastic idea.

"That has already been done," Dick replied, without his usual teasing smile.

"Now who's kidding?" chided Roy.

"No, I mean it, Roy. If you go back twenty-five hundred years you'll find that a powerful king had a special television of the future."

"Nebuchadnezzar, I suppose," spoke the captain, catching Dick's illustration.

"That's right, Captain Tim. Remember the dream of the metal image? We were reading about it last night, Roy. The king sat in his palace thinking of his mighty empire and wondering if it would stand forever. He fell asleep and had a dream, but when he awoke he couldn't remember it. Then Nebuchadnezzar called in his wise men, who were clever fakers; but they couldn't tell him the dream."

"That's where Daniel comes on the scene," added Roy. "The angry king was ready to destroy all his wise men. Soldiers were sent to kill Daniel and his three friends, who had not been called to the palace; but he pleaded for time in order to reveal the dream to the king."

"It must have been exciting for Daniel when he stood before Nebuchadnezzar and said: 'O king, you saw a great image!' Daniel surely had faith that God had given him the true answer."

"You're right, Dick," the man agreed. "I've always thought that Daniel had plenty of courage in that hour."

"He had to face lions, too," suggested Bette.

"What were the nations that were flashed before the king, Captain Tim?" Dick was particularly interested in history. "I know Babylon was the golden head," he added, "but what came after it?"

"The empire that overthrew Babylon was Medo-Persia. In 538 B.C., many years after Nebuchadnezzar died, the Medes and Persians came down to the rich valley of the Euphrates River and surrounded Babylon. Cyrus was the general of the army. Remind me sometime and I'll tell you the thrilling story of his life."

The Hanging Gardens built by King Nebuchadnezzar were a series of stone terraces rising more than three hundred feet high, upon which grew beautiful flowers and shrubs.

"Why not now?" Bette asked.

"It would take us from the answer to Dick's question."

"Yes, let's stick to this story now," urged the boy. "I've wondered what nations Daniel was talking about."

"It is amazing how the city of Babylon was captured by Cyrus," the storyteller continued. "This great city was the wonder of the ancient world. In Nebuchadnezzar's day it was a metropolis three and a half miles long by three miles wide, protected by a wall a hundred feet high and sixty-five feet wide. A highway on top of the wall went around the city so that soldiers could drive chariots along the ramparts. The wall had a hundred huge bronze gates which no enemy could batter down. Through the city flowed the Euphrates River, which furnished water at all seasons of the year."

"They didn't have cannon or guns, did they?" queried Bette.

"No, that was long before the time of modern guns or tanks, Bette. The general could not take Babylon by force, so he waited and planned. He knew that on a certain night the king was giving a great feast in the palace. Cyrus placed some of his troops at the side of the city where the Euphrates River flowed in under the wall. He had other groups of soldiers stationed at the lower side of the city where the river flowed out again. Then the general sent some of his picked troops to open the floodgates above the city and turn much of the river into canals. The water level of the mighty stream began to drop, and when it became low enough, the troops waded into the stream under the wall and came out inside the city."

"That's clever! The old general must have had quite a bag of tricks," said Dick excitedly.

"Wait, Dick, the Persian troops weren't victorious yet," reminded the captain. "There were great walls along the river, and gates where bridges crossed the Euphrates. Even though the soldiers were inside the city they could not reach the streets unless something had gone amiss. In all the excitement of the feasting the Babylonians had forgotten to shut the river gates. The Persians marched in, overcame the guards, entered the palace, and killed Belshazzar. Of course, Daniel was spared and served under the Persian rulers."

Prowling lions wander about through the lonely and deserted ruins of Babylon, the ancient capital of Nebuchadnezzar's empire, which Cyrus captured by entering the city under the river gates.

"That certainly was an exciting conquest," said Dick.

"Didn't Nebuchadnezzar build some Hanging Gardens for his beautiful queen who came from the mountain country?" asked Mrs. Lane. "It seems that I read that somewhere."

"Yes, my dear, history tells us that there were stately parks and gardens in the city. The Hanging Gardens built by the king were a series of stone terraces reaching up to a height of more than three hundred feet. On each terrace was a layer of rich soil, in which flowers, shrubs, fruit trees, and palms grew."

"It was a dry country," commented Dick. "How did they water the gardens?"

"Archaeologists have found that water was pumped to the highest point and then ran down to each terrace. It must have been a wonderful place in hot weather. The royal prince could rest in the shade of the stone balconies, hear the water dripping down into the gardens, and have slaves fan him and play soft music."

"Pretty soft," agreed Roy. "Does anything remain of these Hanging Gardens today?"

"More than most folk suppose," the captain replied. "The foundations have been discovered, and some of the stone arches of beautiful gardens still exist. There seems little doubt that these ruins are part of the Hanging Gardens built by King Nebuchadnezzar long ago for his beloved queen."

"What kingdoms came after Medo-Persia?" asked Dick, not forgetting his original question.

"Oh, yes," Captain Lane went on. "The Greeks overthrew the Persians and became the conquerors of the world. This took place under Alexander the Great. Then Rome brought the downfall of Greece and conquered the world. The iron in the metal image was a good symbol for the Roman Empire, for it was strong and powerful. In A.D. 476 Rome fell, and the kingdom was divided into the parts that have become the various countries of modern Europe. Today we are actually living in the period of history represented by the toes of the metal image."

"If I remember correctly, the next event will take place when the stone strikes the image," said Roy thoughtfully.

"That's correct, my boy," answered the captain. "We are living in the days when the God of heaven shall set up a kingdom that shall never be destroyed. Daniel had faith to speak

God's word, and we should look for the event to take place in our day."

"Let's turn on the television set once more, Timothy, and see what there is on the screen," suggested Mrs. Lane, noticing that the eyes of the young folk were turned toward the set.

"You knew I wanted to, didn't you?"

The man snapped on the switch. "Of course, I could see it all over your face."

The picture formed on the screen was that of a symphony orchestra. As the captain adjusted the dials, the rich music of Beethoven's *Fifth Symphony* came from the loud-speaker. The precision playing of the musicians could be watched as the camera in the auditorium shifted from the conductor to the first violin section.

"This gives you the best seats in the house, Captain Tim," said Bette softly. "I love it."

The group was lost in admiration of the orchestra and the stirring music it rendered.

"If we have many programs like this, I know I'll like our television set," the man admitted with a gay note in his voice. "Nothing is more fascinating to me than a symphony orchestra."

"My English lesson is calling me," said Dick, suddenly remembering tomorrow's school. "Let's get going, Bette, Roy! Mother told us to hurry home."

"As much as I hate to leave this concert, I'll go and study," Bette declared ruefully. And the Barrett trio said good-by quickly, leaving the captain and his wife in front of their new television set.

21

DANIEL in the DEN of LIONS

DANIEL 5:1 to 6:28

KING NEBUCHADNEZZAR died, but the kingdom of Babylon continued in power and greatness. Finally, Belshazzar, grandson of Nebuchadnezzar, was placed in authority in the capital city. This weak ruler was foolish; he loved only pleasure and self-glory. Soon his nation faced grave danger. The armies of the Medes and the Persians came against Babylon.

Belshazzar did not worry about the enemy, for he thought the strong walls of the city would make it impossible for the enemy to enter. He made a great feast and invited a thousand lords to attend. Princes and statesmen drank wine and praised their heathen gods of silver and gold. In the royal banquet hall there was suddenly a hush and then silence. The fingers of a man's hand appeared and began to write on the wall. The king turned pale, and his knees knocked together. He shouted for his wise men to help him. "Whosoever reads this writing, and gives me the interpretation of it," said the king, "shall be clothed with purple, and shall have a chain of gold round his neck, and shall be third ruler in the kingdom."

When the wise men entered the banquet hall and saw the writing on the wall, they were helpless; they could not read it.

(211)

On the night that Cyrus conquered Babylon, King Belshazzar sat at the banquet table with his lords, little dreaming of the fate that awaited him and his great kingdom.

The queen mother heard the cries of Belshazzar and his lords, and she came into the hall. She remembered how Daniel had interpreted the dreams of King Nebuchadnezzar in days gone by. "Let Daniel be called in, then," she said firmly, "and he will give the interpretation."

So Daniel was hurriedly brought before the king. When

Belshazzar saw the aged prophet, he said: "You are Daniel, of the exiles of Judah, whom my father the king brought from Judah! I have heard of you, that the spirit of the gods is in you, and that light, and understanding, and surpassing wisdom are found in you. Now, if you can read the writing, and make known to me the interpretation of it, you shall be clothed with purple, and shall have a chain of gold round your neck, and shall be third ruler in the kingdom."

"Keep your gifts for yourself, and give your rewards to another," said Daniel bluntly; "but I will read the writing to the king, and make known to him the interpretation of it."

Daniel reminded Belshazzar of how his grandfather made the mistake in forgetting God and of the terrible punishment that came upon him. Turning to the writing on the wall, Daniel interpreted the words, saying: "And this is the interpretation of the matter: Mene—God has numbered your kingdom, and brought it to an end; Tekel—you have been weighed in the scales, and found wanting; Peres—your kingdom is divided, and given to the Medes and Persians."

Daniel was clothed in purple, a gold chain was placed around his neck, and he was proclaimed third ruler in the kingdom. But that night the strong army of the Medes and Persians stealthily entered the city, overcame the guards, and killed the king of Babylon. The words written by the divine hand on the wall of the banquet room had come true!

Daniel continued to serve in the court. The conquering ruler, King Darius, made Daniel chief of all his governors. In fact, he considered setting this able man over the whole kingdom. Of course some of the officers were jealous, and they plotted how

When Daniel heard that the decree had been signed, he went to his house, which had windows open toward Jerusalem. He continued to pray to his God three times a day.

they might get Daniel into trouble. Try as hard as they might, they could find no fault with him. Among themselves the jealous officers said: "We shall find no ground of complaint against this Daniel, unless we find it in connection with the law of his God."

Finally the wicked plotters decided upon a plan. They went to King Darius and flatteringly said: "O king Darius, live forever! All the presidents of the kingdom, the prefects and the satraps, the ministers and the governors, have agreed in council that the king should lay down a statute, and pass a strict interdict, to the effect that whosoever shall offer a petition to any god or man for thirty days, except to you, O king, shall be cast into the den of lions. Now, O king, lay down the interdict, and sign the document, so that it may not be changed, in accordance with the law of the Medes and Persians, which is unalterable."

These men knew that Daniel prayed to the God of heaven. They did not mention this to the king, however, for they knew that if he realized that the law would endanger Daniel's life he would not sign the decree. The monarch was proud that his men wanted to worship him as a god, so he signed the decree, and the spies went swiftly to Daniel's house to see what he would do.

When the prophet of God heard that the decree had been signed, he went to his house, which had windows open toward Jerusalem. Three times a day, as was his custom, he knelt and gave thanks to God. When Daniel's enemies saw him in prayer, they hurried to the king's palace. "Did you not sign an interdict," they said, "to the effect that whosoever should offer a petition to any god or man for thirty days, except to you, O king, should be cast into the den of lions?"

"The thing stands fast, in accordance with the law of the Medes and Persians, which is unalterable," said the king.

"This Daniel, of the exiles of Judah, pays no regard to yourself, O king, nor to the interdict which you have signed," said the spies, "but three times a day he continues offering his own petitions."

When King Darius heard this, he was grieved. At once he realized that these officers had planned to trap Daniel. The king worked all day trying to save his faithful governor; but at sunset the crafty officers thronged about the monarch, and said: "You are aware, O king, that it is a law of the Medes and Persians that no interdict or statute which the king lays down can be changed."

(Upper) Beautiful Babylonian wall and gate in mosaic bricks taken from the ancient city ruins and re-built in the Berlin Museum. (Right) One of the guardians of a Babylonian city discovered near the gateway. The figure is represented as sprinkling holy water from a vessel he is carrying.

(Left) Archaeologists discovered this brick wall in the city of Babylon, on which may be seen the relief carvings of sacred animals.

The king was forced to give the royal order, and Daniel was thrown into the den of lions. Before the brave Hebrew officer was put in the den, Darius spoke to him, saying: "May your God, whom you worship so regularly, save you!" Then the den was closed with a great stone, and it was sealed with the king's signet.

That night the king could not sleep. His thoughts were on Daniel in the den of snarling lions. In the morning, as soon as it was light, King Darius hurried to the den and called in a pleading voice: "O Daniel, servant of the living God, has your God, whom you worship so regularly, been able to save you from the lions?"

The king listened. Would there be an answer from the darkness of the den?

"O king, live forever!" replied Daniel. "My God has sent His angel, and has shut the mouths of the lions, so that they have not injured me; because I was found innocent before Him, and before you also, O king, have I done no injury."

The happy king quickly gave orders for his friend to be taken from the lions' den. Darius then commanded that all the men who had accused Daniel should be brought to the lions' den. These wicked officials, with their wives and children, were thrown to the lions. Now the lions were ferocious; they broke the bones of the people before they reached the bottom of the den.

Then Darius wrote this decree to all nations: "Peace be multiplied to you! I hereby make a decree that throughout all the kingdom which I rule men shall tremble in reverence before the God of Daniel."

Daniel, the aged prophet, continued to prosper during the reign of Darius, and he was loyal to God all the days of his life.

22

ESTHER, QUEEN of GREAT COURAGE

THE BOOK OF ESTHER

WHEN Cyrus, who followed Darius as ruler of Medo-Persia, came to the throne, he decreed that the Hebrews scattered through the provinces of Medo-Persia could go back to their homes in Canaan. There were thousands who did not return, and among those who stayed in Persia was Mordecai, a man of the tribe of Benjamin. He was an officer of the king, and in his house at Shushan lived Esther, his cousin. When Esther was a little girl, her father and mother had died, and Mordecai had cared for her as he would his own daughter.

King Xerxes was now the ruler of the Persian Empire. In the Bible he is called Ahasuerus. As he sat in his palace at Shushan, he decided to make a feast for all the people of the city. It was not possible, according to the custom of the country, for men and women to eat together at a banquet. Therefore Queen Vashti made a special dinner for the women. On the last day of the festival King Xerxes commanded the queen to come to his feast so that the men could see her great beauty. But the modest Queen Vashti refused to go to the feast where the drunken men were celebrating. The king was very angry because the queen

(219)

Queen Esther appeared before King Xerxes
as he sat on his golden throne. "What is
your wish, Queen Esther?" asked the king.

W. WILKE, ARTIST

had disobeyed him. Therefore he ruled that she was no longer
to be his queen.

Sometime later the king decided to choose another queen
from among the beautiful maidens of the empire. Messengers
were sent to all the provinces inviting maidens to appear at the
king's palace. Esther, the cousin of Mordecai, was taken to the
palace with the other girls. After months of training she was presented to the king, and he chose her to be his queen.

Esther was loved by her servants and soon became a favorite
in the palace. Since she lived in a royal house, Mordecai could
not visit with her. Nevertheless, every day he walked to and fro
in the courtyard near her window.

As an officer of the king, Mordecai sat at the palace gate. One
day he overheard the plot of two angry servants. They were planning to kill King Xerxes. Mordecai sent a message to Queen
Esther, and she told the king. The men were soon discovered in
their treachery and hanged.

About this time, Haman, a proud prince of the court, was
promoted, and the king commanded that the other officers
should bow to him. Mordecai would not bow to Haman, for he
had been taught to worship God alone. When the servants saw
that Mordecai refused to bow, they told Haman. This proud
man was filled with rage, but he did not dare lay hands on the
loyal officer. What could he do? Soon he decided upon an evil
plan. Since Mordecai was a Jew, Haman approached King
Xerxes and said: "There is a certain people scattered abroad and
dispersed among the peoples throughout all the provinces of
your kingdom, and their laws are different from every other people; neither do they observe the king's laws; therefore it is not

That night King Xerxes could not sleep. To help him pass the hours, his servants brought the records and read them to him. He was surprised to learn of Mordecai's act.

fitting to leave them alone. If it please the king, let it be prescribed that they be destroyed; and I will pay ten thousand talents of silver into the hands of those who do the accounting, that they may bring it into the king's treasuries."

The king did not know the evil purpose of Haman, for he trusted this high officer to do what was right. Furthermore, he did not know that Queen Esther was a Jew. King Xerxes signed the letter commanding the nation to kill all the Jews on a certain day, and messengers carried the edict to all the empire.

When Mordecai heard of the decree, he tore his garments and mourned deeply. He knew that this law doomed his people to destruction. There was only one hope. Perhaps Esther could save these innocent and helpless men and women.

Queen Esther learned that Mordecai was mourning. She did not know what was wrong, so she sent him beautiful garments. However, Mordecai would not accept them, and finally he told the servant to tell Esther what was about to happen to her people. The queen was stunned by the message from Mordecai. What could she do? The law said that no one could come before the king who was not summoned by him, unless the monarch held out his golden scepter to him.

Trusting in the Lord to help his people, Mordecai sent this word to the queen: "Think not to yourself that you will escape inside the royal palace any more than all the rest of the Jews. For if you remain altogether silent at this time, then relief and deliverance will rise up for the Jews from another quarter, but you and your father's house will perish; and who knows whether you have not come to the kingdom for such a time as this?"

When Esther received this challenge, she sent a message back to Mordecai: "Go, assemble all the Jews that are to be found in Shushan and fast for me," said Esther. "And neither eat nor drink for three days, night or day. I also and my maidens will likewise fast, and then I will go to the king, which is not according to the law; and if I perish, I perish."

On the third day Queen Esther put on her beautiful robes and went to the door of the throne room. King Xerxes, seated on his throne, saw the queen. He held out his golden scepter, and Esther drew near and touched it. "What is your wish, Queen Esther?" asked the king. "It shall be given you even to the half of the kingdom."

"If it please the king," said Esther, "let the king and Haman come today to a banquet that I have prepared for him."

So the king and Haman came to the banquet that Esther had prepared. Then the king asked Esther what she desired. The queen replied demurely: "My petition and my request is: If I have found favor in the sight of the king, and if it please the king to grant my petition, and to perform my request, let the king and Haman come to my banquet that I shall prepare for them, and tomorrow I will do as the king has said."

Haman was so proud to be the special guest of the queen that he rushed home to tell his wife what had happened. "Even Esther the queen," said Haman, "has permitted no man but me to come in with the king to the banquet that she has prepared, and tomorrow also I am invited by her together with the king. Yet all this does not satisfy me so long as I see Mordecai the Jew sitting at the king's gate."

Haman's wife and his friends proposed that a high gallows be built and that in the morning he ask the king for permission to hang Mordecai. Haman liked the idea, and he had the gallows erected at once.

That night the king could not sleep. To help him pass the hours he had his servants bring the records of the kingdom and read them to him. Now in the record was the account of the two traitors who had planned to kill the king and of how Mordecai had saved Xerxes' life.

"What honor and dignity have been bestowed on Mordecai for this?" asked the king.

"Nothing has been done for him," said the servant, scanning the records carefully.

By this time it was early morning. Haman had risen and made his way to the palace to request the death of Mordecai. At

"Make haste, and take the garments and the horse, as you have said," Xerxes commanded Haman, "and do even so to Mordecai the Jew who sits at the king's gate."

that moment his footsteps were heard in the hall. The king, thinking of the traitors who had once almost taken his life, called out: "Who is in the court?"

A servant announced: "Behold, Haman is standing in the court."

"Let him enter," said the king.

So Haman came in, and the king said to him: "What shall be done to the man whom the king delights to honor?"

Haman said to himself: "Whom would the king delight to honor more than myself?" So the proud man tried to picture all the things he would like to have. "For the man whom the king delights to honor," said Haman, "let royal garments be brought, which the king has worn, and a horse which the king has rid-den, on the head of which a royal crown is set. Let the garments and the horse be delivered to one of the king's most noble princes, and let them clothe the man whom the king delights to honor and cause him to ride on horseback through the open square of the city, and proclaim before him, 'Thus shall it be done to the man whom the king delights to honor.'"

"Make haste, and take the garments and the horse, as you have said," commanded the king, "and do even so to Mordecai the Jew who sits at the king's gate. Let nothing fail of all that you have spoken."

Haman's mouth must have dropped open in surprise. He must lead a horse through the streets with Mordecai riding upon it in royal splendor! The honor that he had dreamed should come to him had fallen upon his hated enemy. Haman rushed home weeping because of what had happened. When his wife heard the news, she wisely said: "If Mordecai, before whom you have begun to fall, be of the Jewish race, you will make no headway against him, but will surely fall before him."

It was the day of Queen Esther's second banquet. "Whatever your petition, Queen Esther, it shall be granted you," said Xerxes, while he and Haman were enjoying the party.

"If I have found favor in the sight of the king, and if it please the king, let my life be given me at my petition and my people at my request," pleaded Esther; "for we are sold, I and my people, to be destroyed, to be slain, and to perish."

"Who is he, and where is he who dares presume in his heart to do so?" asked the king.

"An adversary and an enemy, this wicked Haman," said Esther, pointing to the cruel officer at the table beside them.

Haman was terrified when he saw how angry the king looked. Xerxes rose from the banquet and strode out into his garden. He now saw through the evil plot of Haman to kill all of the innocent people. At once the king was in a rage; he would punish this prince for his wicked deeds. A servant who stood near the king suggested: "There is indeed the gallows fifty cubits high standing in the house of Haman, which Haman has made for Mordecai, who spoke good in behalf of the king."

"Hang him on it," said the king curtly, and thus Haman's fate was sealed.

Then Xerxes sent special messengers riding swiftly to all provinces in the empire telling the Jews to gather in groups and fight for their lives on the day that had been set for their destruction. The Jews gathered in armed bands; but when their enemies heard of the king's second decree, they did not dare attack the Jews. Angels of God protected His people while they stood bravely for their lives. Thus Esther had saved the lives of her people and her own life by her faithfulness in time of grave danger.

When the Jews who were doomed to die heard the second decree, they thanked God for salvation and stood bravely for their lives.

An ATTEMPTED MURDER

T AKE these ten squares of cardboard and write a number on each. Begin with 1 and go to 10."

"What is this—a game?" asked Roy, as he followed Captain Lane's instructions.

The Barrett trio had dropped in to see the captain in his basement workshop. They had told him the latest news from school and what they were planning to do during the coming Christmas vacation.

"No, it isn't a game," replied the man. "You said you were puzzled because your teacher declared that our world and everything in it came by chance. I don't believe that, and neither do you. It reminds me of these ten bits of cardboard."

"How's that?" queried Bette, trying to follow her friend's logic.

"Put those ten squares of cardboard in the shoe box, Bette, and shake it well."

"O.K.," the girl replied, following instructions, "but it gets more mysterious every minute."

"If you draw those squares out of the box, what are your chances of getting them in perfect order?" asked the man as he worked at his bench.

(229)

The Greek army halted before Jerusalem, for Alexander had come to punish the Jews for siding with Persia in the long war.

W. WILKE, ARTIST

"I'd say about one in a thousand," ventured Roy.

"You'll have to try again, young man," the captain replied. "Your chances of drawing No. 1 is one in ten. That you might draw 1 and 2 in succession is one in a hundred. Your chances of drawing 1, 2, 3, 4 in order would be one in ten thousand."

"To get 1 to 10 in perfect order would be almost impossible, then." Dick gave his opinion cautiously.

"How right you are! To be mathematical, your chances would be one in ten billion that you could pick those pieces of cardboard out in their correct order," Captain Lane said with a smile. "If that is true about ten simple squares of cardboard, how can people be so foolish as to say that our world just happened? The planets move in perfect order. Nature reveals her wonders in plant and animal life, and the human body is a marvel of design. These couldn't just happen. Every wonder of science proves that there must be a God who created all things."

For a moment the captain stopped talking while he studied the electric heater he was attempting to repair. Then he turned once more to his young friends. "There is something else that proves there is a God."

"What's that?"

"Bible prophecies. I promised you a story about the Persian general, Cyrus. If you have time, I'll tell you now about it, for his experience proves to me that things don't just happen."

"Let's hear it," Dick said eagerly. "We are all ears!"

"Yes, go ahead, Captain Tim. I don't need to be home for another half hour," agreed Bette, looking at her watch.

"Would you please run up to the study, Roy, and get my Bible? I'll need it," said the man.

Cyrus, named in Bible prophecy before his birth, led his soldiers into the palace and captured the royal family. That night the empire of Babylon fell to the Medo-Persians.

"Yes, sir." Roy was up the stairs two at a time.

When he returned, the captain continued. "Suppose you made a prediction about a man more than a hundred years before he was born, do you think it would be possible that you could make a mistake?"

"It wouldn't be possible for us to make such predictions," Bette said emphatically.

"Suppose you called him by name," the man continued, turning the pages in the Bible as he talked.

"Sounds like fiction to me," Dick commented.

"God made a prediction about Cyrus, the warrior, more than a hundred years before he was born. Here is the prophecy in Isaiah 45:1. You read it, Bette."

The girl took the Bible and began to read: " 'Thus saith the Lord to His anointed, to Cyrus, whose right hand I have holden, to subdue nations before him; and I will loose the loins of kings, to open before him the two-leaved gates; and the gates shall not be shut.' That says that the gates would be open for Cyrus. Does that mean that it was predicted the gates of Babylon would be left open?"

"That's exactly right, Bette, and you remember that's what happened on the night of Belshazzar's feast," replied the captain. "Now read the fourth verse."

Once more the girl took the Bible and read: " 'For Jacob My servant's sake, and Israel Mine elect, I have even called thee by thy name: I have surnamed thee, though thou hast not known Me.' "

"That's a daring prediction, isn't it, Captain Lane?"

"Yes, indeed, Roy. Don't you see, too, that if the enemy of truth could cause this prediction to fail, God's word would be proved false? That's exactly what Satan tried to do. He did his best to kill Cyrus before the prediction could come to pass."

"Tell us all about it, Captain Tim. It gets more exciting all the time," urged Dick.

The man seated himself in an old rocker in the corner of the workshop, propped up one foot on an apple box, and began his story. "You see, it was back in the days of ancient Media, the country that had a king named Astyages. One night the ruler had a dream, and in his vision he saw a great river which not only flowed over his capital but it filled all Asia. His wise men told him that it meant that the children of his daughter, Mandane, would someday become mighty conquerors. This

The city of Babylon fell to the arm'es
Cyrus. The soldiers entered through
gates that had carelessly been left unlocke

W. WILKE, ART

displeased the king so that he arranged for his daughter to marry a Persian named Cambyses who seemed content without power. Thus Astyages thought he would make Media and Persia friendly countries, but never would they be joined. The dream was repeated sometime later, and again the old king was worried, for his wise men said it meant that Mandane's son would rule Asia. A royal grandson was born to his daughter about this time, so the evil, selfish king decided that the young heir to the throne should be killed and thus stop the dream from coming true. This baby boy was named Cyrus."

"Is this the Cyrus who captured Babylon?" asked Bette.

"The same man. Now, when the baby was brought to the palace, he was decked in the gorgeous golden trappings of a prince. King Astyages decided that he must act at once. Calling a trusted servant, Harpagus, he told him to take the child away and kill him and bring the body back to the palace."

"What a horrible thing for the grandfather of the child to do," said Dick in anger.

"Yes, but this is only the beginning. The servant was afraid to kill the royal heir, so to shift the responsibility he called in a herdsman from the mountain country and instructed him to expose the baby in the winter weather until he was dead and then bring the body back to him. Harpagus would then take it to the king. The poor herdsman took the healthy young baby to his house. There he found his wife crying, for their own newly born son had just died. Now to have his own child die and to have the terrible job of killing this beautiful baby was too much for the herdsman. Therefore he made a plan and secretly carried it out.

"He dressed the body of his own dead child in the royal clothes and took it back to Harpagus, who returned it to the king. Thus old Astyages was satisfied, thinking that Cyrus, his grandson, was dead."

"This sounds fantastic. What happened to the baby?" asked Roy, sitting down on the arm of the captain's rocking chair.

"Cyrus grew up in the house of the herdsman. When he was about twelve years old he was playing war with his young friends. Cyrus was the general and one of the boys, the son of a nobleman, refused to obey, so Cyrus proceeded to give the youngster a good thrashing. The whipped boy told his father, who in turn took the matter up with the king. They decided to call in the peasant boy who had whipped the son of a nobleman. When Cyrus stood before the king, Astyages was impressed at once by the clean-cut features and the independence of the lad. He noted, too, that the boy was about the age his own grandson would be if he had not been put to death.

"The king questioned Cyrus, but of course the boy knew nothing about his experience. The whole thing haunted the king's conscience, and he called in the herdsman. After torture and threats, the herdsman told the whole story. Astyages hid his anger against his trusted servant, Harpagus, but swore in his heart to get revenge. He dismissed the herdsman and sent Cyrus to his own mother and father in Persia, for he knew that he could not now murder the boy."

"Did the king get revenge on Harpagus for deceiving him?" asked Dick, anxious to hear the rest of the story.

"He did. One day he called the servant to him and said that he was making a great banquet that evening. With pomp and ceremony the king asked Harpagus to attend the feast. Before time for the banquet a messenger came to Harpagus requesting that he send his own young son to the palace to serve the king."

"Why did Astyages ask that?"

"You'll soon see. Anyway, the banquet was a great success; the king's trusted servant, Harpagus, was given the best place, and what is more, choice dishes of meat were placed before him. At the close of the meal the king asked him how he had enjoyed the dinner. The servant expressed his pleasure and appreciation. Then the wicked heathen king showed how he had taken revenge on Harpagus. He brought a basket to his servant, and in it were the head and hands and feet of his son. The king had killed the servant's son and made him eat some of the boy's flesh."

"The wicked old man! What a fiend!" Bette pounded the workbench with a hammer to give vent to her feelings.

"Wasn't he, though!" chimed in Roy and Dick.

"Harpagus silently endured this unspeakable torture," the captain continued. "But he swore that he would someday take revenge. Years passed by, and at last Harpagus sent a messenger to Cyrus in Persia, who had grown to be a mighty warrior. He told Cyrus how he as a babe had been saved from death and of what Astyages had done to his son. He asked Cyrus to come against Media, conquer the land, and take the king a prisoner. Cyrus read the message and decided to act. For some time he had dreamed of marching against the country of Media and uniting it with Persia, and here was his opportunity. Soon the capital was captured. The wicked King Astyages was taken prisoner, and Harpagus was revenged. But the important part

The king's trusted servant, Harpagus, attended the royal banquet, where he was served many choice dishes. Then the wicked king revealed what he had served to his guest.

of the story is that Cyrus became the mighty general who eventually conquered Babylon. From the time he was born, the evil one had designed to kill him; but God protected His servant and guarded him through the years.

"A few years after Cyrus conquered Media, he looked toward the mighty empire of Babylon and determined to take that country. It was hopeless from the human point of view, but Cyrus marched against the city, and you know of his clever plan. Remember, too, that the giant gates leading into the city from the river were left open that night by the guards who were more intent on pleasure than in protecting their country."

"That is just what the prophecy of Isaiah said would happen, isn't it?" asked Dick eagerly.

"Yes, and it was all fulfilled to the letter by Cyrus, the pagan warrior. Later on, God used this same man to help the Jews return to Jerusalem."

"Where did you get that story—from history?" asked Dick.

"Yes, Dick, from Herodotus, the famous Greek who has been called 'the father of history.' In many instances his pagan writings confirm the truthfulness of the Bible. That's why I say prophecy is another great proof that there is a God. He has told us what would come to pass hundreds and even thousands of years before it happened, and it has always been fulfilled to the letter. If only one point in that prophecy could have been set aside by the evil one, the Bible would not be true. God named the man; He told him what his work would be; and He told how the gates would be open so that he could march in and take the city. There were many 'chances' for error in the prophecy, yet no human hand could have invented it, for it was fulfilled to the letter."

"That's a thrilling story," commented Roy. "I'm going to tell that to my teacher sometime. Perhaps that will help make it plain to her that the Bible is true and that God directs our lives. Things don't happen just by chance."

"That's right, Roy," agreed the captain earnestly. "And remember that text in Isaiah 40:8 which says: 'The grass withereth, the flower fadeth: but the word of our God shall stand forever.' "

"After everything else disappears, the Bible still stands," Dick declared with emphasis. "There is no other book like it."

"That's right, there is no other book like it," chimed in Bette.

Memory Verses

"Daniel purposed in his heart that he would not defile himself with the portion of the king's meat, nor with the wine which he drank." Daniel 1:8.

"As for these four children, God gave them knowledge and skill in all learning and wisdom: and Daniel had understanding in all visions and dreams." Daniel 1:17.

"If it be so, our God whom we serve is able to deliver us from the burning fiery furnace, and He will deliver us out of thine hand, O king." Daniel 3:17.

"My God hath sent His angel, and hath shut the lions' mouths, that they have not hurt me: forasmuch as before Him innocency was found in me; and also before thee, O king, have I done no hurt." Daniel 6:22.

"Then Esther bade them return Mordecai this answer, Go, gather together all the Jews that are present in Shushan, and fast ye for me, and neither eat nor drink three days, night or day: I also and my maidens will fast likewise; and so will I go in unto the king, which is not according to the law: and if I perish, I perish." Esther 4:15, 16.

"He hath made the earth by His power, He hath established the world by His wisdom, and hath stretched out the heaven by His understanding." Jeremiah 51:15.

23

The RETURN to JERUSALEM

THE BOOKS OF EZRA AND NEHEMIAH

KING NEBUCHADNEZZAR burned the city of Jerusalem and destroyed Solomon's temple when he took the people of Judah as captives to Babylon. For years the Jews lived in exile in a far-off country, but they never forgot their homeland. Because they had disobeyed the Lord and worshiped idols, He had allowed them to fall into the hands of their enemies. But, after years of captivity, the people of Judah realized what it meant to be without a temple where they might worship God and offer sacrifices, and they determined never to worship idols again. They wept when they thought of the ruins of the once glorious city of Jerusalem.

When the army of Cyrus surrounded Babylon during the reign of Belshazzar, the captives took hope. They knew the prophecy that had been written by Isaiah more than a century before the birth of Cyrus, declaring that this man would free the exiles and help them return to their homes. With joy they read again these words:

> "Thus says the Lord to His anointed,
> To Cyrus, whose right hand I have grasped,
> To bring down nations before him,
> And to ungird the loins of kings,

oldiers guarded the workmen who were
ebuilding the temple. Enemies from Samaria tried to hinder the work from going on.

, WILKE, ARTIST

To open doors before him,
And that gates may not be closed:
'I will go before you,
And will level the rugged heights;
The doors of bronze will I break in pieces,
And the bars of iron will I cut asunder;
I will give you the treasures of darkness,
The hoards of secret places;
That you may know that I am the Lord,
That I who have called you by name am the
      God of Israel.' "

The Lord also told Isaiah that Cyrus would rebuild Jerusalem. This prophecy came to pass in the first year of the reign of Cyrus, the Persian, when he made this decree: "Thus says Cyrus, king of Persia: 'All the kingdoms of the earth has the Lord, the God of the heavens, given me, and He has commissioned me to build Him a house in Jerusalem, which is in Judah. Whoever there is among you of all His people who desires to go, his God be with him; let him go up to Jerusalem, which is in Judah, and build the house of the Lord, the God of Israel, since He is the God who is in Jerusalem. Whoever is left in any place where he resides as an alien, let the men of his place aid him with silver and gold and goods and beasts of burden, as well as with voluntary offerings for the house of God which is in Jerusalem.' "

None of the Jews were forced to return to the land of Canaan. Families could choose to go or stay as they wished. Zerubbabel, a descendant of King David, was placed in charge of the caravan, and the high priest Joshua stood by his side to help.

Across the hot and dreary desert the caravan made its way. When the people arrived in Jerusalem, they built an altar on the

Across the hot and dreary desert the caravan made its way. When the people arrived in Jerusalem, they built an altar and gave thanks to God for bringing them safely home.

site where Solomon's temple had stood and they gave thanks to God for bringing them safely back to their own country.

Workmen made preparations to rebuild the temple. Many of the great stones that had been the foundation in the house of the Lord which Solomon had built were found in the rubble and made ready for use. When the day came to lay the cornerstone of the new temple, the people sang and shouted for joy.

While the work of rebuilding the temple and the city walls was going on, enemies from Samaria came and attempted to hinder the project. Work was stopped for a time; but, with the help of another Persian king, the temple was finally completed. However, the walls and houses of the city continued to lie in ruins for many years.

Now in the court of King Artaxerxes of Persia there was a Jew named Nehemiah who was the king's cupbearer. This servant had to taste the drink that was offered to the ruler to prove that there was no poison in it. While Nehemiah was at the court in Shushan, he prayed and fasted, asking the God of heaven to help his people restore the kingdom of Judah. King Artaxerxes saw his servant's troubled look and asked: "Why is your countenance sad, since you are not ill? This is nothing else but sorrow of heart."

Nehemiah was frightened because the king had noticed his sadness. "Let the king live forever!" exclaimed Nehemiah. "Why should not my countenance be sad, when the city, the place of my fathers' sepulchers is desolate, and its gates have been destroyed by fire."

"For what then do you make request?" the king said.

"If it please the king," said Nehemiah, with a prayer in his heart, "and if your servant be acceptable in your sight, that you would send me to Judah to the city of my fathers' sepulchers, that I may rebuild it."

The king acted favorably on Nehemiah's request and sent him on his way to Jerusalem with an escort of soldiers and letters to the governors through whose provinces he would pass on his long trip. He also carried gifts to help pay the cost of rebuilding the city.

After the king's cupbearer had been in Jerusalem for three days, he decided to survey the state of the work. He tells in these words what he did: "Then I arose in the night, I and a few men with me, but I told no man what my God had put in my heart to do for Jerusalem, neither was there any beast with me except the beast on which I rode. Accordingly I went out by night through the Valley Gate, even toward the Serpent's Well and to the Refuse Gate, and I examined in detail the walls of Jerusalem, which were broken down, and its gates destroyed by fire. So I passed on to the Fountain Gate and to the King's Pool, but there was no place for the beast that was under me to pass. Then I went on up in the night along the valley, examining the wall, whereupon I turned back and entered by the Valley Gate, and so returned; and the rulers did not know where I had gone or what I had been doing, neither had I as yet told it to the Jews, nor to the priests, nor to the nobles, nor to the rulers, nor to the rest who did the work."

Then Nehemiah gathered the leaders together and courageously said: "Let us arise and build."

The cupbearer of King Artaxerxes organized the work, and, in spite of enemies, the wall of Jerusalem was soon completed.

The people of Judah were settled once more in their little kingdom. The second temple was not as beautiful as Solomon's had been, since many of the treasures had not been restored. The most holy place was empty, for the golden ark containing the Ten Commandments on tablets of stone had been hidden by Jeremiah when the city was about to be captured, and it was never found again.

24

A NATION RESTORED

ALTHOUGH many families from the tribes of Judah and Benjamin returned to Jerusalem, yet thousands of Jews remained in Persia and Egypt after they were released from bondage. In these lands they became successful in business and commerce.

The people who returned to Jerusalem no longer worshiped idols. They loved the true God and served Him with complete loyalty. Jerusalem once more became a great center as Jews came from their homes in distant lands to worship God in the new temple.

As long as the Persians ruled the world, the people of Judah were safe from invasion. However, a new world empire came into being in 331 B.C., when Alexander the Great defeated the Persians. Soon the Greek army marched south to capture Jerusalem, for Alexander had decided to punish the Jews for siding with Persia in the long war. When Alexander's army approached the city, Jaddua, the high priest, and all the temple priests marched out through the gates in solemn procession to meet the victorious leader. When the Jews surrendered to the Greek army, Alexander was so impressed with their dignity and honesty that he saluted the high priest. Thousands of people

The captive Jews hung their harps on the branches of the willow trees and
sat by the river of Babylon, weeping for Jerusalem and its departed glory.

saw the kind act of the general, and they shouted for joy. Alexander and Jaddua entered Jerusalem together, and Alexander offered sacrifices in the temple. The Greek leader gave the nation many freedoms, and the land was secure until Alexander the Great died.

In 170 B.C., Antiochus Epiphanes came to the throne of Greece. He was determined to force the Jews to accept the pagan religion and to worship idols. After conquering Egypt, he led his army to Jerusalem, broke down the walls, massacred thousands of Jews, and burned much of the city. He robbed the holy Temple of its golden furniture and made a mockery of the worship of the Lord.

The Jews were forbidden to offer sacrifices, and they were not allowed to keep the holy Sabbath. Nevertheless, thousands of faithful men and women stood firm and refused to disobey the commandments of the Lord, preferring to die rather than sin against God.

When officers of Antiochus tried to enforce the tyrant's orders, they were opposed by Mattathias, a priest of the temple. His five sons stood with their father, grimly determined to gain freedom for their nation at any cost. When the enemy soldiers came to the high priest and offered him riches and honor if he would renounce his allegiance to God, Mattathias said: "If all the heathen in the king's dominions listen to him and forsake each of them the religion of his forefathers, and choose to follow his commands instead, yet I and my sons and my brothers will live in accordance with the agreement of our forefathers. God forbid that we should abandon the law and the ordinances."

When he stopped speaking, a Jew stepped forward to offer a sacrifice to a Greek idol, and Mattathias sprang forward and killed the man. In the fight that followed, he also slew the officer of Antiochus. This started a fierce revolution, led by a son of Mattathias, Judas Maccabaeus.

Soon the Romans became rulers of the world. In 63 B.C. the Roman general Pompey captured Jerusalem. Many faithful Jews were killed defending the city and the Temple, but Pompey did not plunder the holy place nor take away any of its treasures.

When the Roman governor Herod the Great ruled Judea, he tried to gain the favor of the Jews by rebuilding the temple.

He was an evil, ambitious ruler, and many of the Jews hated him. It was during his reign that Jesus, the Son of Mary, was born in Bethlehem.

Thus, for hundreds of years the Jewish nation had looked for the coming of the promised Messiah. For hundreds of years they had read the prophecies concerning the mighty Deliverer who would save His people. The little town of Bethlehem, where David grew up, was to be the birthplace of the Messiah. Micah, the prophet of God, had said:

> "And you, O Bethlehem Ephrathah,
> Too little to be among the clans of Judah,
> From you, One shall come forth for Me,
> Who shall be ruler over Israel,
> Whose origins are from of old,
> From ancient days."

All Judah was waiting for the coming of the Son of God who would save His people from their sins.

Captain Tim's Bible Quiz

"It's time for you to make out some questions to see if we are really learning our Old Testament," said Bette Barrett to the captain one day as she was chatting with him in his study.

"All right, we'll begin with the story of the prophet Jeremiah and end with the close of the Old Testament history. I'll make twenty questions that will make your brain cells hum," said jovial Captain Tim. His list of questions may have some puzzlers for you. After you have answered them, check with the correct answers on page 253.

1. What did King Jehoiakim do with Jeremiah's message that was written on a scroll?
2. What Babylonian king captured Jerusalem and took many prisoners to Babylon?
3. What was the first test that Daniel and his companions faced when they entered Nebuchadnezzar's court in Babylon?
4. Where did the evil princes put Jeremiah when they attempted to get rid of him because he warned Jerusalem of its doom?
5. Who were placed in the burning fiery furnace because they would not bow down to the golden image of Nebuchadnezzar?
6. What nation captured Babylon during the night while Belshazzar was holding the great feast?
7. What did Daniel continue to do after Darius made the decree that no one should worship any god except the Medo-Persian king?
8. Who was the fourth person that Nebuchadnezzar saw in the burning fiery furnace with the three Hebrews?
9. How was Daniel saved from the lions?
10. Who was the queen of King Xerxes before he chose Esther for the royal position?
11. Who was hanged on a gallows he had made for his enemy?
12. What Persian king was named in Bible prophecy long before he was born?

13. What was the position of Nehemiah in King Artaxerxes' court?

14. Who was the high priest when Alexander marched into Jerusalem and accepted the city's surrender?

15. What happened to King Nebuchadnezzar when he refused to obey God and continued as a proud and haughty ruler?

16. Of what five substances was the great image made which King Nebuchadnezzar saw in his dream?

17. What was the message of the handwriting on the wall, which Belshazzar saw the night Babylon fell?

18. What honor did King Xerxes bestow upon Mordecai for having saved his life from enemies?

19. What king brought reforms in Judah when Jeremiah was a young man?

20. To what country were Jeremiah and Baruch taken against their will?

Answers to Bible Quiz

NUMBER I, PAGE 83

The correct answer, the Bible reference, and the page in this book where the facts are found are listed below.

1. Kish. 1 Samuel 9:1, 2. Page 21.
2. Bethlehem. 1 Samuel 16:18, 19. Page 35.
3. "God save the king." 1 Samuel 10:24. Page 17.
4. Abner. 1 Samuel 14:50. Page 31.
5. Goliath. 1 Samuel 17:4, 51. Page 42.
6. Holy bread. 1 Samuel 21:4. Page 55.
7. Benjamin. 1 Samuel 9:21. Page 22.
8. Giant Goliath's sword. 1 Samuel 21:9. Page 55.
9. En-dor. 1 Samuel 28:7, 8. Page 63.
10. Jerusalem. 2 Samuel 5:5. Page 80.
11. Hebron. 2 Samuel 2:3, 4. Page 79.
12. Uzzah. 2 Samuel 6:7. Page 82.
13. Michal. 1 Samuel 18:20, 21. Page 52.
14. Psalm 23. Page 72.
15. Agag. 1 Samuel 15:9. Page 32.
16. Jonathan. 1 Samuel 18:1. Page 51.
17. Water from the well of Bethlehem. 2 Samuel 23:16. Pages 60, 61.
18. By playing on the harp. 1 Samuel 16:23. Page 37.
19. Ramah. 1 Samuel 7:17. Page 21.
20. Feast of Tabernacles. Leviticus 23:39, 40. Page 47.

NUMBER II, PAGE 169

The correct answer, the Bible reference, and the page in this book where the facts are found are listed below.

1. Mephibosheth. 2 Samuel 9:6, 7. Page 85.
2. Nathan. 2 Samuel 12:1. Page 86.
3. General. 2 Samuel 18:2. Page 92.
4. Carmel. 1 Kings 18:20. Page 118.
5. Jezreel. 1 Kings 18:45. Page 121.
6. Absalom. 2 Samuel 15:10. Page 89.
7. An understanding heart. 1 Kings 3:9. Page 99.
8. Forty years. 1 Kings 2:11. Page 97.

9. Queen of Sheba. 1 Kings 10:1, 2. Page 100.
10. Elisha. 1 Kings 19:19. Page 122.
11. Bread and meat. 1 Kings 17:6. Page 116.
12. Jezebel. 1 Kings 19:2. Page 121.
13. Axhead. 2 Kings 6:5. Page 130.
14. Hiram. 1 Kings 5:1. Page 100.
15. Nineveh. Jonah 3. Page 148.
16. Naaman. 2 Kings 5:9, 14. Page 133.
17. Ahimaaz. 2 Kings 18:22. Page 93.
18. Smitten with blindness. 2 Kings 6:18, 19. Page 140.
19. Bath-sheba. 1 Kings 1:11. Page 96.
20. Gold, silver, ivory, apes, and peacocks. 2 Chronicles 9:21. Page 102.

───────────────── NUMBER III, PAGE 250 ─────────────────

The correct answer, the Bible reference, and the page in this book where the facts are found are listed below.

1. Cut it with a penknife and burned it. Jeremiah 36:23. Page 178.
2. Nebuchadnezzar. Jeremiah 37:1. Page 181.
3. Diet. Daniel 1:5. Page 189.
4. Into a cistern. Jeremiah 38:6. Page 183.
5. Shadrach, Meshach, and Abednego. Daniel 3:20. Page 195.
6. Medo-Persia. Daniel 5:30, 31. Page 213.
7. Pray. Daniel 6:11. Page 215.
8. "One of the gods," or the Son of God. Daniel 3:25. Page 196.
9. An angel shut their mouths. Daniel 6:22. Page 217.
10. Vashti. Esther 1:9. Page 219.
11. Haman. Esther 7:10. Page 227.
12. Cyrus. Isaiah 44:28; 45:1. Page 231.
13. King's cupbearer. Nehemiah 2:1. Page 244.
14. Jaddua. Page 246.
15. Lost his mind. Daniel 4:33. Page 199.
16. Gold, silver, brass, iron, and clay. Daniel 2. Page 193.
17. God has numbered your kingdom, and brought it to an end; you have been weighed in the scales, and found wanting; your kingdom is divided, and given to the Medes and Persians. Daniel 5:26-28. Pages 212, 213.
18. Commanded Haman to escort him through the streets on the king's horse. Esther 6:11. Page 225.
19. Josiah. 2 Kings 22:2-5. Page 171.
20. Egypt. Jeremiah 43:5-7. Pages 184, 185.